mep Mathematics Enhancement Pr
Demonstration Project

Practice Book: Y7B

Principal Author: Ted Graham, Centre for Teaching Mathematics, Plymouth University

Senior Editor: David Burghes, Centre for Innovation in Mathematics Teaching

Advisors:	Graham Bryant	Caldicot Comprehensive School, Monmouthshire
	Chris Graddon	Streetly School, Sutton Coldfield, West Midlands
	Chris Hall	Hassenbrook School, Stanford-le-Hope, Essex
	Malcolm Jenkin	Penair School, Truro, Cornwall
	Mary Ledwick	Our Lady and St John High School, Blackburn
	Graham Middleton	Stanchester Community School, Stoke-sub-Hamdon, Somerset
	Adrian Smith	Penair School, Truro, Cornwall

| *Checkers:* | Nigel Oates |
| | Albine Patterson |

Typesetter: Liz Holland

This is one component of MEP Mathematics resources for Y7.

All enquiries regarding these resources should be addressed to

Mathematics Enhancement Programme
CIMT, Institute of Education
Plymouth University
Drake Circus   Tel: 01752 585346
Plymouth PL4 8AA   Fax: 01752 586520

First printing   February 2001

Published by **CIMT, Plymouth University**

Copyright © **CIMT, Plymouth University**

ISBN: 978-1-910171-01-1

Design by *Clinton Banbury*
P.O. Box 2892, Billericay, Essex CM11 2LF
Tel: 01277 630421

Contents

13 Searching for Pattern

13.1 Pictorial Logic

In this section we will see how to continue patterns involving simple shapes.

Example

Continue these patterns by drawing the next 5 shapes in each case:

(a)

(b)

Solution

(a) This pattern consists of four shapes that repeat in the same order. The repeating pattern is:

The pattern can now be extended:

(b) This pattern consists of increasing numbers of squares separated by triangles. The pattern can be extended by adding 4 squares and another triangle:

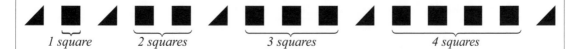

1 square   2 squares   3 squares   4 squares

Exercises

1. Add the next 5 shapes to each of the repeating patterns below:

   (a)

   (b)

   (c)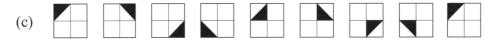

   (d)

2. Add the next 5 shapes to each of these patterns:

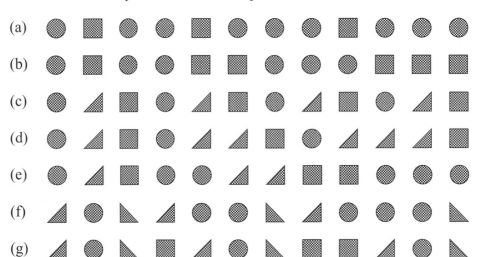

   (a)

   (b)

   (c)

   (d)

   (e)

   (f)

   (g)

   (h)

3. Extend each pattern until you obtain a shape that is 5 squares long:

   (a)

   (b)

   (c)

   (d)

   (e)

   (f)

4.   Consider the pattern of shapes shown below:

   ⊙ ▦ ◿ ⊙ ▦ ◿ ⊙ ▦ ◿ ⊙ ▦ ◿

   (a)   What is the 3rd shape in the pattern?

   (b)   What is the 15th shape in the pattern?

   (c)   What is the 30th shape in the pattern?

   (d)   What is the 31st shape in the pattern?

5.   Consider this pattern of shapes:

   ⊙ ◿ ▦ ◣ ⊙ ◿ ▦ ◣ ⊙ ◿ ▦ ◣

   (a)   Draw the 8th shape.

   (b)   Draw the 20th shape.

   (c)   Draw the 21st shape.

   (d)   Draw the 19th shape.

6.   Consider this pattern of shapes:

   ⊙ ▦ ⊙ ▭ ⊙ ▭ ⊙ ▭ ⊙

   (a)   What is the 11th shape?

   (b)   What is the 21st shape?

   (c)   What is the 41st shape?

   (d)   How long is the 4th shape?

   (e)   How long is the 6th shape?

   (f)   How long is the 20th shape?

7.   Look at this pattern:

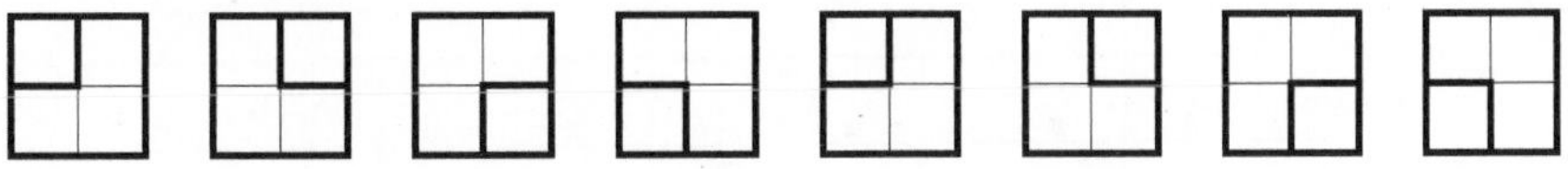

   (a)   Draw the 4th and 8th shapes.

   (b)   Draw the 16th shape.

   (c)   Draw the 17th shape.

   (d)   Draw the 40th shape.

   (e)   Draw the 38th shape.

8. The diagram shows the 5th to 14th shapes in a pattern:

5th 6th 7th 8th 9th 10th 11th 12th 13th 14th

Draw and label the first 4 shapes in the correct order.

9. The diagram shows the 6th to 15th shapes of a pattern:

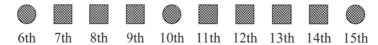

6th 7th 8th 9th 10th 11th 12th 13th 14th 15th

Draw and label the first 5 shapes of the pattern.

10. Fill in the missing shapes in this pattern. There should be one shape for each number.

△ ◣ △ ○
1   2   3   4   5   6   7   8   9   10

◣ △ ○ ○ ○ ○ ◣
11 12 13 14 15 16 17 18 19 20

13.2 Extending Number Sequences

You will have studied some sequences in Unit 7. This section takes these ideas further and introduces some other types of sequences.

Example

The first 4 triangular numbers are represented by the diagrams below:

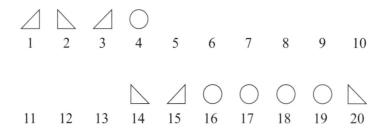

1   3   6   10

(a) Draw the next 3 triangular numbers.

(b) Describe how to find the 8th, 9th and 10th triangular numbers without drawing the diagrams.

Solution

(a) Note that an extra row of dots is added to each triangle and that the extra row has one more dot than the previous row. The next 3 triangular numbers are shown below:

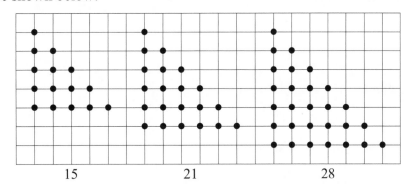

(b) To extend the sequence of triangular numbers, look at the difference between the terms:

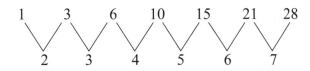

Note that the difference between each term increases by 1 as you move along the sequence.

So,

$$\text{8th term} = 28 + 8$$
$$= 36$$

$$\text{9th term} = 36 + 9$$
$$= 45$$

$$\text{10th term} = 45 + 10$$
$$= 55$$

Example

Write down the next 3 terms of the sequence:

$$3, \ 7, \ 10, \ 17, \ 27, \ 44, \ 71, \ \ldots$$

Solution

Look at the differences between each term:

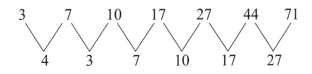

The first difference is not very helpful, but then note how the sequence of differences is the same as the original sequence.

For example, $10 + 7 = 17$

To find the next 5 terms:

$$8\text{th term} \quad = \quad 71 + 44$$
$$= \quad 115$$

$$9\text{th term} \quad = \quad 115 + 71$$
$$= \quad 186$$

$$10\text{th term} \quad = \quad 186 + 115$$
$$= \quad 301$$

In this type of sequence, called a *Fibonacci* sequence, each term is the sum of the two previous terms. For example, this sequence begins:

$$3, \ 7, \ 10 \quad \text{where} \quad 3 + 7 = 10$$

and the next term is $10 + 7 = 17$.

Triangular Numbers	1, 3, 6, 10, 15, 21, 28, . . .
Square Numbers	1, 4, 9, 16, 25, 36, 49, . . .
Cubic Numbers	1, 8, 27, 64, 125, . . .
Fibonacci Sequence	1, 1, 2, 3, 5, 8, 13, . . .
(formed by adding the two previous terms to get the next one)	

Exercises

1.   Write down the next 4 terms of each of these sequences:

   (a)   4, 7, 10, 13, 16, 19, . . .

   (b)   5, 11, 17, 23, 29, 35, . . .

   (c)   6, 8, 11, 15, 20, 26, . . .

   (d)   8, 10, 14, 20, 28, 38, . . .

   (e)   24, 23, 21, 18, 14, 9, . . .

   (f)   2, 12, 21, 29, 36, 42, . . .

   (g)   1, 1, 2, 4, 7, 11, . . .

2.   The diagram shows the first 4 square numbers:

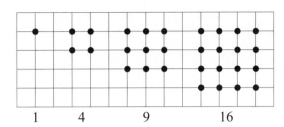

1	4	9	16

(a)   Draw the next 2 square numbers, and write their actual value underneath.

(b)   What is the 10th square number?

(c)   What is the 20th square number?

(d)   Find the differences between each of the first 6 square numbers in turn. What would be the difference between the 6th and 7th square numbers? Check that your answer is correct by drawing the 7th square number.

3.   (a)   Write down the next 3 terms in each of these sequences:

(i)   0, 3, 8, 15, 24, . . .   (ii)   2, 5, 10, 17, 26, . . .

(iii)   11, 14, 19, 26, 35, . . .   (iv)   6, 9, 14, 21, 30, . . .

(b)   In each case above, explain how the sequence is related to the sequence of square numbers 1, 4, 9, 16, 25, . . . , . . .

4.   For each sequence below, draw the next two diagrams and write down the number of dots in each of the first 10 diagrams:

(a)

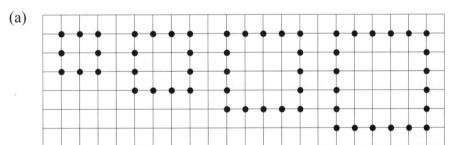

(b)

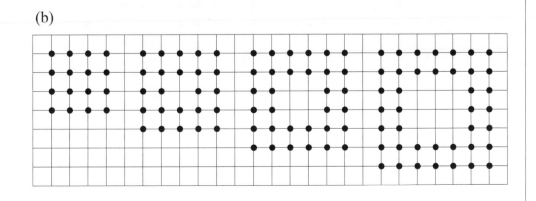

(c)

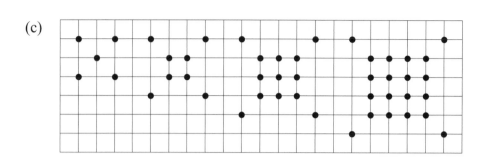

5. For each sequence below, draw the next 3 diagrams and write down the number represented by each of the first 8 diagrams:

    (a)

    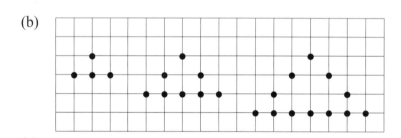

    (b)

    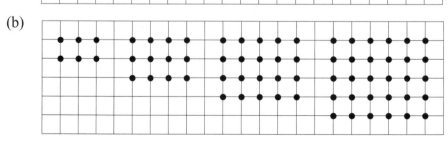

    (c)

6. What number is represented by the 10th diagram in each of the sequences illustrated in the following diagrams:

    (a)

    (b)

(c)

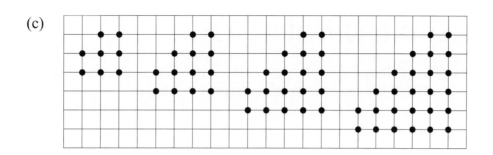

7. The Fibonacci sequence begins:

   1, 1, 2, 3, 5, 8

   Calculate the 10th and 20th terms in this sequence.

8. Write down the next 5 terms in each of these sequences:

   (a)   2, 2, 4, 6, 10, . . .

   (b)   1, 3, 4, 7, 11, . . .

   (c)   2, 5, 7, 12, 19, . . .

   (d)   1, 9, 10, 19, 29, . . .

9. Write down the missing terms in each sequence:

   (a)   ☐ , ☐ , 5, 9, 14, 23, 37, ☐ , ☐ , . . .

   (b)   ☐ , ☐ , ☐ , ☐ , 20, 33, 53, 86, 139, . . .

   (c)   ☐ , ☐ , ☐ , ☐ , 7, 11, 18, 29, 47, . . .

10. A sequence begins:

    1, 2, 3, 6, 11, 20, 37, 68, . . .

    (a)   What do you get if you add: (i)   the first three terms,

                                      (ii)   the 2nd, 3rd and 4th terms,

                                      (iii) the 3rd, 4th and 5th terms?

    (b)   What are the next 3 terms in the sequence?

    (c)   A similar sequence is given below. Write down the missing terms.

          ☐ , ☐ , ☐ , 14, 26, 48, 88, 162, . . .

    (d)   A sequence begins:

          1, 1, 3, 5, 9, 17, 31, . . .

          Write down the next 3 terms in the sequence.

13.3 Patterns and Matchsticks

In this section we look at forming patterns with matches, to generate sequences. We then look at how to describe these sequences.

Example 1

(a) Draw the next three shapes in this sequence:

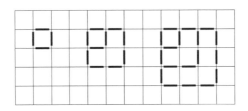

(b) How many matches are used in each shape?

(c) How many matches are used in the 10th shape?

Solution

(a) Here is the sequence with the next 3 shapes:

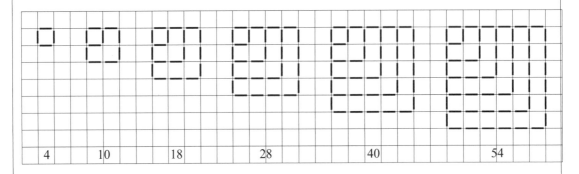

(b) The number of matches is written under each shape.

(c) The sequence is listed here with the differences between terms:

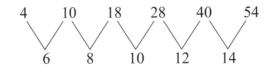

Note how the differences increase by 2 as the sequence continues.

The 6th term is 54.

The 7th term is $54 + 16 = 60$.

The 8th term is $60 + 18 = 78$.

The 9th term is $78 + 20 = 98$.

The 10th term is $98 + 22 = 120$.

Example 2

The diagram shows the first 3 shapes in a pattern made from matches:

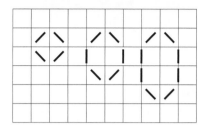

(a)   Draw the next 3 shapes and state how many matches are used to make each shape.

(b)   Write down the 10th and 20th terms in this sequence.

(c)   What is the *n*th term in this sequence?

(d)   One shape needs 20 matches. Which one is it?

Solution

(a)   The diagram shows the next 3 shapes:

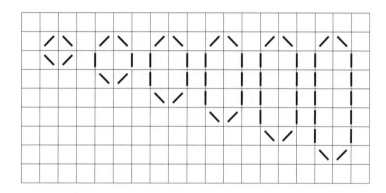

The number of matches in each shape is listed below:

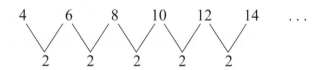

Notice that the difference between each term is 2.

(b)   Note that:

$$1\text{st term} \qquad 4 \;=\; 2 + 2 \times 1$$

$$2\text{nd term} \qquad 6 \;=\; 2 + 2 \times 2$$

$$3\text{rd term} \qquad 8 \;=\; 2 + 2 \times 3$$

$$4\text{th term} \qquad 10 \;=\; 2 + 2 \times 4$$

So to find the 10th term,

$$2 + 2 \times 10 \;=\; 22$$

and the 20th term,

$$2 + 2 \times 20 \;=\; 42$$

(c)   The nth term is $2 + 2 \times n = 2 + 2n$.

(d)   For the shape that needs 20 matches, we need to find the missing number in the calculation:

$$2 + 2 \times \boxed{} = 20$$

The missing number is 9.

We can write this in steps:

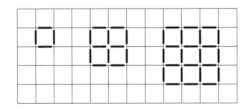

$$2 + 2 \times \boxed{} = 20$$

$$2 \times \boxed{} = 18$$

$$\boxed{} = 9$$

Exercises

1.   Here is a pattern formed with matches:

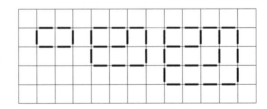

(a)   Draw the next 3 shapes.

(b)   How many matches are used in each of the first 6 shapes?

(c)   How many matches are needed for each of the 7th and 8th shapes?

2.   Here is a pattern of shapes made with matches:

(a)   Draw the next 3 shapes.

(b)   How many matches are needed for the 10th shape?

(c)   Which shape needs 97 matches?

3. How many matches are needed to make the 8th shape in this pattern?

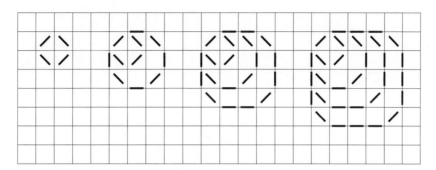

4. A pattern of rectangles is made using matches:

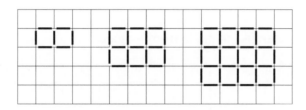

   (a) Draw the next two rectangles.

   (b) How many matches would be needed for the 7th rectangle?

   (c) Which rectangle requires 199 matches?

5. The shapes below are made using matches:

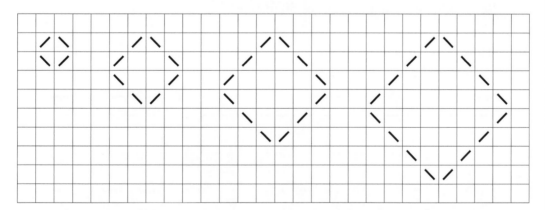

   (a) How many matches would be needed for each of the 5th and 6th shapes?

   (b) How many matches would be needed for the *n*th shape?

   (c) Which shape contains 88 matches?

6.   How many matches would the *n*th shape in the pattern below contain?

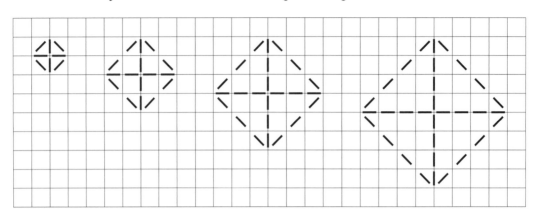

7.   A pattern of rectangles is made from matches:

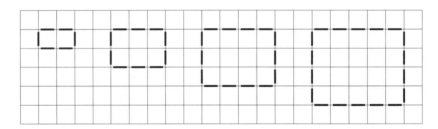

    (a)   How many matches are needed for the 10th rectangle?

    (b)   How many matches are needed for the *n*th rectangle?

    (c)   Which rectangle requires 50 matches?

8.   How many matches are needed to make the *n*th shape in the pattern of rectangles below?

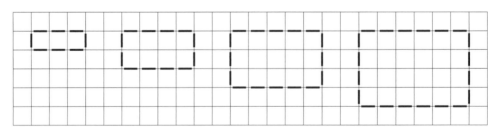

9.   A pattern of shapes is made from matches:

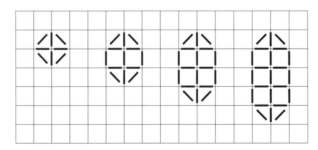

Write down:

(a)   the number of matches in each of the 5th and 10th shapes,

(b)   the number of matches in the *n*th shape.

10.   How many matches are needed to make the *n*th shape of each of these patterns?

(a)

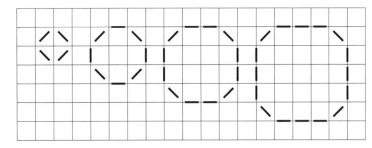

(b)

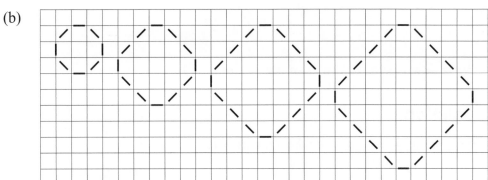

(c)

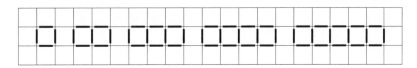

(d)

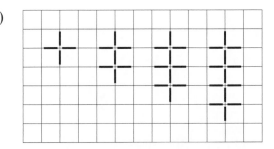

(e)

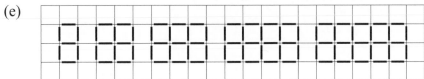

(f)

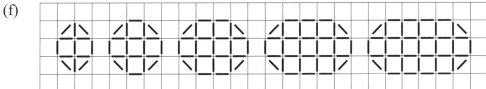

13.4 Two-Dimensional Number Patterns

This section explores 2-dimensional number patterns. One of the most famous of these is *Pascal's triangle*.

Example 1

Here are the first 4 rows of Pascal's triangle.

```
        1
      1   1
    1   2   1
  1   3   3   1
```

Write down the next 3 rows of the triangle.

Solution

Note that each row starts and ends with a 1.

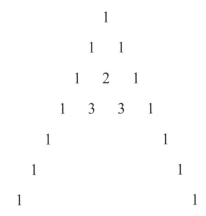

The other numbers are found by adding together the two numbers that are diagonally above them in the previous row.

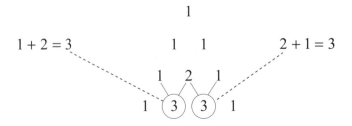

Using this rule the triangle can be completed:

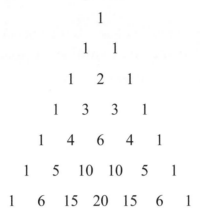

```
                    1
                 1     1
              1     2     1
           1     3     3     1
        1     4     6     4     1
     1     5    10    10     5     1
  1     6    15    20    15     6     1
```

Example 2

What are the next 2 diagrams in the sequence:

```
    1    ,    1   1   ,    1   1   1   ,   ...
              2             2   2
                                4
```

Solution

Note how the numbers in the next row are obtained by adding together two of the numbers in the row above.

For example, in the 2nd diagram, $1 + 1 = 2$

and in the 3rd diagram, $2 + 2 = 4$.

Using this rule, the sequence can be extended:

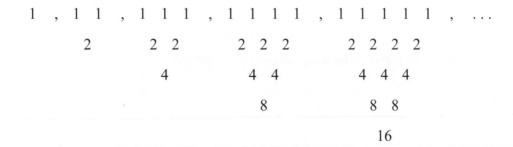

```
 1  ,  1  1  ,  1  1  1  ,  1  1  1  1  ,  1  1  1  1  1  ,  ...
          2        2  2        2  2  2        2  2  2  2
                      4           4  4           4  4  4
                                     8              8  8
                                                      16
```

Exercises

1. In example 1, the first 7 rows of Pascal's triangle are listed. By adding the next 3 rows, write down the first 10 rows of the triangle.

2. Patterns can be found in the diagonals of Pascal's triangle. Copy the part of the triangle shown here and add the next 4 terms to the three diagonals shown.

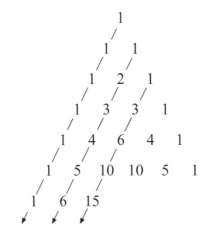

3. Write down the next two diagrams in the sequence:

```
2   ,   2  2  ,   2  2  2  ,   . . .
        4           4  4
                       8
```

4. Write down the next three diagrams in this sequence:

```
1   ,   1  2  ,   1  2  3  ,   . . .
        3           3  5
                       8
```

5. Write down the next three diagrams in the sequence:

```
1  ,  1  2  ,  1  2  1  ,  1  2  1  2  ,  . . .
      3           3  3           3  3  3
                     6              6  6
                                      12
```

6. Write down the next three diagrams in the sequence:

```
1  ,  1   3  ,  1   3   5  ,  . . .
      4          4   8
                  12
```

7. Here are the first 5 rows of a triangle of numbers:

```
                    2
                 2     2
              2     4     2
           2     6     6     2
        2     8    12     8     2
```

(a) Write down the next 3 rows of the triangle.

(b) Explain why the triangle contains no odd numbers.

8. Here are the first three diagrams in a sequence:

```
   3    ,    3   3   ,    3   3   3   ,   . . .
             6            6   6
                         12
```

(a) What is the next diagram in the sequence?

(b) What is the largest number in the 5th diagram in the sequence?

(c) What is the largest number in the 10th diagram in the sequence?

(d) For which diagram is the largest number 384?

9. Here is a sequence of number diagrams:

```
   1   ,    1   2   ,    1   2   3   ,   . . .
            2            2   6
                        12
```

Write down the next 2 diagrams in this sequence.

10. Write down the next 3 diagrams in this sequence:

```
   1 , 1   2 , 1   2   3 , 1   2   3   4 , 1   2   3   4   5 ,
       3       3   5       3   5   7       3   5   7   9
           8           8   2           8   2   6
                           0               0   8
                                               8
```

What is the largest number that will appear in any of the diagrams of this sequence?

14 Time and Timetables

14.1 Telling the Time

In this section we look at different ways of writing times; for example, '7:45' is the same time as 'quarter to eight'.

On a clockface, this can be represented as shown here:

minute hand

hour hand

Also remember that

> one hour = 60 minutes

so that

> half an hour = 30 minutes
>
> quarter of an hour = 15 minutes
>
> three quarters of an hour = 45 minutes

Example 1

Write each time using digits and show the position of the hands on a clockface:

(a) twenty five past eight,

(b) quarter to ten.

Solution

(a) Twenty five past eight using digits is

8:25

(a) Quarter to ten can be thought of as:

15 minutes to 10 o'clock

or

45 minutes past 9 o'clock

so, using digits, quarter to ten is

9:45

Example 2

Write each of the times shown on these clocks:

(i)   in words,   and   (ii)   using digits.

(a) 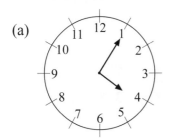   (b) 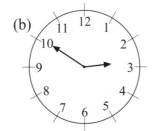   (c)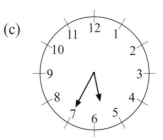

Solution

(a)   (i)   Five past four   (ii)   4:05

(b)   (i)   Ten to three   (ii)   2:50

(c)   (i)   Twenty five to six   (ii)   5:35

Exercises

1.   Write the times shown on each of these clocks in words and digits:

(a) 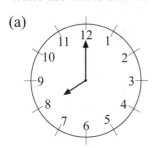   (b) 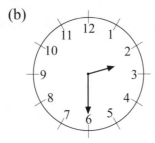   (c)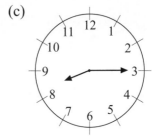

(d) 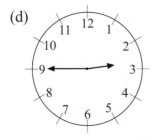   (e) 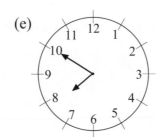   (f)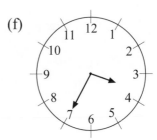

(g) 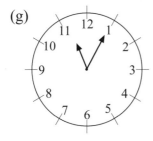   (h) 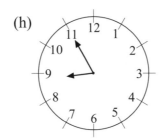   (i)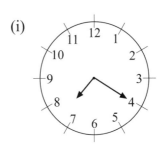

2.   Draw these times on clock faces:

    (a)   ten past five   (b)   ten to nine   (c)   quarter to seven

    (d)   quarter past twelve (e)   half past ten   (f)   twenty to nine

    (g)   ten to two   (h)   twenty five to six (i)   twenty past four

3.   Draw these times on clock faces:

    (a)   4:00   (b)   5:30   (c)   7:15

    (d)   8:20   (e)   2:45   (f)   3:50

    (g)   1:55   (h)   6:05   (i)   11:35

4.   Write these times in words:

    (a)   9:30   (b)   4:00   (c)   4:25

    (d)   8:45   (e)   7:35   (f)   9:05

5.   Write these times using digits:

    (a)   eight o'clock   (b)   quarter to seven

    (c)   ten past five   (d)   half past six

    (e)   ten to three   (f)   five to four

    (g)   twenty five to nine   (h)   twenty to three

6.   This picture shows the time
    on Vicki's radio clock:

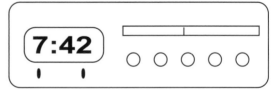

    (a)   Draw a picture to show where the hands would be on this clock:

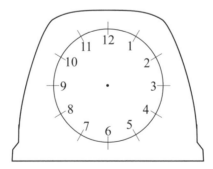

    (b)   Write the time in words.

7. Daniel's digital watch has gone wrong and shows a grey blob instead of the first digit of the minutes.

   Use the ordinary clock to tell Daniel what the missing digit is for each of the times shown below:

(a)

(b)

(c)

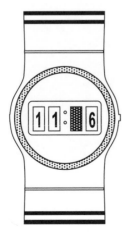 

(d)

8.   Halim looks at his watch and sees that the time is 7:46.

    (a)   Write this time in words.

    (b)   What will be the time 10 minutes later?

9.   A bus leaves school at five minutes past four and Tony gets off 20 minutes later. What is the time when Tony gets off the bus? Write your answers in words and in figures.

14.2   12- and 24-hour Clocks

The 24-hour clock system can be used to tell if times are in the morning or the afternoon. Alternatively, times can be given as 'a.m.' or 'p.m.'

Example 1

Write these times in 24-hour clock time:

(a)   3.06 a.m.   (b)   8:14 p.m.

Solution

(a)   As this is an 'a.m.' time it remains the same but with a zero in front of the 3,

        0306

(b)   As this is a 'p.m.' time, add 12 to the hours to give

        2014

Example 2

Write these times using 'a.m.' or 'p.m':

(a)   1428   (b)   0742

Solution

(a)   As the hours figure, 14, is greater than 12, subtract 12 and write as a 'p.m.' time:

2:28 p.m.

(b)   As the hours figure, 07, is less than 12, simply remove the zero and write as an 'a.m.' time:

7:42 a.m.

Exercises

1.   Convert these times to 24-hour clock times:

(a)   9:42 a.m.   (b)   11:28 p.m.   (c)   11:14 a.m.

(d)   7:13 p.m.   (e)   9:21 p.m.   (f)   4:18 p.m.

(g)   10:05 a.m.   (h)   12:15 a.m.   (i)   12:15 p.m.

2.   Write these times in 24-hour clock time:

(a)   quarter to eight in the morning,   (b)   ten minutes to midnight,

(c)   ten past nine in the evening,   (d)   five to seven in the morning,

(e)   quarter past five in the afternoon, (f)   half past two in the afternoon.

3.   Write these 24-hour clock times in 12-hour clock times, using 'a.m.' or 'p.m.':

(a)   1204   (b)   0822   (c)   1842

(d)   1330   (e)   1440   (f)   2305

(g)   1735   (h)   1605   (i)   0342

4.   Write these 24-hour clock times in words, as in question 2:

(a)   1430   (b)   1555   (c)   0745

5.   Insert 'a.m.' or 'p.m.' into each sentence so that it makes sense:

(a)   Joshua woke up at 6:45.

(b)   Miles came home from school at 3:55.

(c)   Andy started his night shift at 10:15.

(d)   Grace ate her lunch at 11:45.

(e)   James went to bed at 8:55.

(f)   Heidi cooked a meal at 5:15.

6.   Here are the timings for a school day.

Convert them to 24-hour clock times.

Registration	8:55 a.m.
Lesson 1	9:05 a.m.
Lesson 2	10:05 a.m.
Lesson 3	11:05 a.m.
Lunch	12:05 p.m.
Lesson 4	1:05 p.m.
Lesson 5	2:05 p.m.
Day ends	3:05 p.m.

7.   A train leaves at 0020. Write this time in words.

8.   Shamil leaves home at 0900 and returns 7 hours later. Write the time that Shamil gets home in 24-hour clock time, and in 12-hour clock time using 'a.m.' or 'p.m.'.

14.3   Units of Time

In this section we explore the different units of time.

1 minute	=	60 seconds
1 hour	=	60 minutes
1 day	=	24 hours
1 week	=	7 days
1 year	=	365 days (366 days in a leap year)
January	has	31 days
February	has	28 days (29 days in a leap year)
March	has	31 days
April	has	30 days
May	has	31 days
June	has	30 days
July	has	31 days
August	has	31 days
September	has	30 days
October	has	31 days
November	has	30 days
December	has	31 days

Example 1

How many hours are there in May?

Solution

Number of hours in May $= 31 \times 24$

$= 744$ hours

Example 2

25 February is a Friday. What will be the date on the next Friday:

(a)   if it is *not* a leap year,

(b)   if it *is* a leap year?

Solution

(a)   You could write out the next 7 days like this:

Friday	25
Saturday	26
Sunday	27
Monday	28
Tuesday	1
Wednesday	2
Thursday	3
Friday	4

or

$25 + 7 = 32$

$32 - 28 = 4$

So the next Friday will be 4 March.

(b)   Using the addition method:

$25 + 7 \; = 32$

$32 - 29 = 3$

So, in a leap year, the next Friday will be 3 March.

Exercises

1. How many hours are there in a week?

2. How many hours are there in:

    (a) September,

    (b) February (2 answers needed),

    (c) one year (2 answers needed)?

3. How many minutes are there in:

    (a) one day,   (b) one week?

4. How many seconds are there in:

    (a) one hour,   (b) one day?

5. If 25 March is a Friday, what will be the date on the following Friday?

6. Sasha goes on holiday on Monday 20 June. She returns 14 days later. On what date does she return from her holiday?

7. If 3 October is a Monday:

    (a) what day of the week will 1 November be,

    (b) what will be the date of the first Monday in November?

8. Hannah goes to the bank every Tuesday. The last time she went was on Tuesday 20 October.

    (a) What will be the dates of her next 2 visits to the bank?

    (b) On the second Tuesday in November she is ill and goes to the bank on Wednesday instead. What is the date of that Wednesday?

9. This year Mike's birthday is on a Saturday in June. What day will his birthday be on next year if:

    (a) next year is a leap year,

    (b) next year is *not* a leap year?

10. In 1998, Christmas Day was on a Friday. Name the day of the week for Christmas Day in:

    (a) 1997,

    (b) 2000.

11. (a) For how many days have you been alive?

(b) How many *hours* is this?

(c) How many *minutes* is this?

(d) How many *seconds* is this?

(e) David has been alive for approximately 1 892 160 000 seconds. In which year do you think he was born?

14.4 Timetables

In this section we consider how to extract information from timetables.

Example 1

London	Bristol Parkway - Cardiff - Swansea Cheltenham - Bath - Bristol									
Sundays from 26 July										
London Paddington	d	1903	1915	1930	2000	2030	2100	2130	2200	2215
Reading	d	1935	1945	2003	2030	2100	2130	2200	2230	2245
Didcot Parkway	d	1949	–	2017	2044	2114	2144	2214	2244	2259
Swindon	d	2009	2015	2036	2103	2133	2203	2233	2303	2319
Kemble	a	2022	–	–	–	–	–	2250	–	–
Stroud	a	2037	–	–	–	–	–	2305	–	–
Stonehouse	a	2042	–	–	–	–	–	2310	–	–
Gloucester	a	2053	–	–	–	–	–	2323	–	–
Cheltenham Spa	a	2108	–	–	•	–	–	2335	–	–
Chippenham	d	–	–	2049	–	2145	–	2245	–	2332
Bath Spa	a	–	2035	2105	–	2157	–	2257	–	2343
Bristol Parkway	d	–	–	–	2129	–	2229	–	2329	–
Bristol Temple Meads	a	–	2051	2117	–	2211	–	2311	–	2357
Weston-super-Mare	a	–	2110	–	–	–	–	–	–	0018
Newport	a	–	–	–	2149	–	2249	–	2353	–
Hereford	a	–	–	–	–	–	–	–	–	–
Cardiff Central	a	–	–	–	2205	–	2305	–	0014	–
Bridgend	a	–	–	–	2225	–	2325	–	0034	–
Port Talbot Parkway	a	–	–	–	2237	–	2337	–	0046	–
Neath	a	–	–	–	2244	–	2344	–	0053	–
Swansea	a	–	–	–	2257	–	2357	–	0106	–

a: arrives   d: departs

Use the train timetable above to answer these questions:

(a) If you catch the 1915 from London Paddington, at what time would you arrive in Weston-super-Mare?

(b) Ted arrives in Chippenham at 2245. At what time did he leave London Paddington?

(c) Tina catches the 2205 at Cardiff Central. At what time does she arrive in Neath?

Solution

(a)   The 1915 from London Paddington arrives at Weston-super-Mare at 2110.

Sundays from 26 July

London Paddington	d	1903	1915
Reading	d	1935	1945
Didcot Parkway	d	1949	–
Swindon	d	2009	2015
Kemble	a	2022	–
Stroud	a	2037	–
Stonehouse	a	2042	–
Gloucester	a	2053	–
Cheltenham Spa	a	2108	–
Chippenham	d	–	–
Bath Spa	a	–	2035
Bristol Parkway	d	–	–
Bristol Temple Meads	a	–	2051
Weston-super-Mare	a	–	2110
Newport	a	–	–

(b)   To arrive in Chippenham at 2245 Ted must have left London Paddington at 2130.

Sundays from 26 July

London Paddington	d	1903	1915	1930	2000	2030	2100	2130
Reading	d	1935	1945	2003	2030	2100	2130	2200
Didcot Parkway	d	1949	–	2017	2044	2114	2144	2214
Swindon	d	2009	2015	2036	2103	2133	2203	2233
Kemble	a	2022	–	–	–	–	–	2250
Stroud	a	2037	–	–	–	–	–	2305
Stonehouse	a	2042	–	–	–	–	–	2310
Gloucester	a	2053	–	–	–	–	–	2323
Cheltenham Spa	a	2108	–	–	-	–	–	2335
Chippenham	d	–	–	2049	–	2145	–	2245
Bath Spa	a	–	2035	2105	–	2157	–	2257
Bristol Parkway	d	–	–	–	2129	–	2229	–

(c)   The 2205 from Cardiff Central arrives in Neath at 2244.

Sundays from 26 July

London Paddington	d	1903	1915	1930	2000
Reading	d	1935	1945	2003	2030
Didcot Parkway	d	1949	–	2017	2044
Swindon	d	2009	2015	2036	2103
Kemble	a	2022	–	–	–
Stroud	a	2037	–	–	–
Stonehouse	a	2042	–	–	–
Gloucester	a	2053	–	–	–
Cheltenham Spa	a	2108	–	–	-
Chippenham	d	–	–	2049	–
Bath Spa	a	–	2035	2105	–
Bristol Parkway	d	–	–	–	2129
Bristol Temple Meads	a	–	2051	2117	–
Weston-super-Mare	a	–	2110	–	–
Newport	a	–	–	–	2149
Hereford	a	–	–	–	–
Cardiff Central	a	–	–	–	2205
Bridgend	a	–	–	–	2225
Port Talbot Parkway	a	–	–	–	2237
Neath	a	–	–	–	2244
Swansea	a	–	–	–	2257

Exercises

1. The table below gives the timetable for a ski train that runs from London Waterloo International:

London Waterloo International	depart	0857
Ashford International	depart	1006
Moûtiers	arrive	1657
Aime la Plagne	arrive	1723
Bourg-St-Maurice	arrive	1742

    (a) At what time does the train leave Ashford International?

    (b) At what time does the train arrive at Bourg-St-Maurice?

    (c) Where does the train arrive at 1657?

    (d) John arrives at London Waterloo International at five past nine. Can he catch the train?

2. The timetable below gives the times of early morning trains from Norwich to London Liverpool Street:

NORWICH	Dep	0500	0520	0530	0600	0630	0655	0710	0755	0805	0835	0905
Diss	Dep	0518		0547	0618	0647	0713	0728	....	0823	0852	0922
Stowmarket	Dep	0531	....	0558	0630	0658	0725	0740	....	0835	0903	0933
IPSWICH	Arr	0541	0553	0610	0641	0709	0736	0751	0828	0846	0913	0944
	Dep	0543	0553	0612	0642	0710	0737	0752	0830	0847	0915	0945
Manningtree	Dep	0553	....	0620	0652	0721	......	0802	....	....	0925	....
COLCHESTER	Dep	0604	0610	0632	0704	0732	....	0812	....	0906	0935	1003
Chelmsford	Dep	....	....	....	....	....	....	....	....	....	....	1020
LIVERPOOL STREET	Arr	0653	070	0721	0756	0826	0848	0903	0933	0955	1025	1054

    (a) At what time does the 0630 from Norwich arrive at Liverpool Street?

    (b) Jason arrives by train at Liverpool street at 0903. At what time did he catch the train at Diss?

    (c) If you catch the 0655 from Norwich, at what time do you arrive at Ipswich?

    (d) Alex arrives at Ipswich station at 0900 and catches the next train to Liverpool Street. At what time does he arrive at Liverpool Street?

    (e) Scott catches the 0612 at Ipswich. At what time does he arrive at Manningtree?

3. The timetable below gives information about trains from London Waterloo to Paris:

Waterloo International	0508	0619	0723	0753	0823	0853	0953	1023	1053	1157
Ashford International	0616	0719	0823	....	0923	....	1053	....	....	....
Calais-Fréthun	....	0856	....	....	....	....	....	....	....	1429
Lille Europe	....	....	....	....	....	1150	....	....	....	....
Paris Nord	0923	1023	1123	1147	1223	1253	1353	1417	1453	1556

(a) Scott arrives in Paris at 1123. At what time did he leave Waterloo?

(b) Chelsea arrives in Paris at 1223. At what time did she leave Ashford?

(c) Jai wants to go from Waterloo to Lille Europe. Which train should he catch?

(d) Halim wants to arrive in Calais-Fréthun before 9:00 a.m. Which train should he catch?

4. Mike is in Brussels and wants to return to Ashford. He looks at this train timetable:

Brussels to Waterloo

Brussels Midi	0856	1102	1302	1456	1702	1756	1856	2102
Lille Europe	0937	1142	1342	1536	1742	1836	1936	2142
Ashford International	0938	1141	1341	1536	1741	1837	1938	....
Waterloo International	1047	1247	1447	1639	1843	1939	2039	2239

(a) At what time should he catch a train if he wants to arrive in Ashford at 1741?

(b) Which train should he *avoid* if he wants to go to Ashford?

(c) If he catches the 1456, at what time does he arrive in Ashford?

(d) He catches the 1456, but falls asleep and does not get off at Ashford. At what time does he get to Waterloo?

5. Use the following timetable to answer these questions:

(a) Rachel catches the 1600 at Reading. At what time does she arrive in Bristol?

(b) Emma catches the 1330 at London Paddington. At what time does she arrive in Bristol?

(c) Hannah arrives in Newport at 1545. At what time did she leave Reading?

(d) Ben arrives at Neath at 1451. At what time did he leave Swindon?

London	Bristol Parkway - Cardiff - Swansea Cheltenham - Bath - Bristol									
Sundays from 26 July										
London Paddington	d	1152	1200	1230	1300	1330	1400	1430	1500	1530
Reading	d	1222	1230	1301	1330	1403	1430	1500	1530	1600
Didcot Parkway	d	–	1244	1314	–	1417	–	1514	1544	1614
Swindon	d	1252	1303	1333	1358	1437	1458	1533	1603	1633
Kemble	a	–	1320	–	–	–	–	1559	–	–
Stroud	a	–	1335	–	–	–	–	1614	–	–
Stonehouse	a	–	1340	–	–	–	–	1619	–	–
Gloucester	a	–	1353	–	–	–	–	1632	–	–
Cheltenham Spa	a	–	1409	–	–	–	–	1644	–	–
Chippenham	d	–	–	1346	–	1449	–	1545	–	1645
Bath Spa	a	–	–	1358	–	1501	–	1557	–	1701
Bristol Parkway	d	–	1329	–	1424	–	1524	–	1629	–
Bristol Temple Meads	a	1324	–	1412	–	1515	–	1611	–	1713
Weston-super-Mare	a	–	–	1432	–	1543	–	1651	–	1751
Newport	a	–	1349	–	1445	–	1545	–	1649	–
Hereford	a	–	–	–	1605	–	1720	–	1820	–
Cardiff Central	a	–	1412	–	1508	–	1608	–	1705	–
Bridgend	a	–	1432	–	1528	–	1628	–	1725	–
Port Talbot Parkway	a	–	1444	–	1540	–	1640	–	1737	–
Neath	a	–	1451	–	1547	–	1647	–	1744	–
Swansea	a	–	1504	–	1559	–	1659	–	1757	–

6.

Penzance - Plymouth - Torbay - Exeter - Taunton - Reading		London								
Sundays										
Penzance	d	–	–	–	–	–	0832	–	0926	0926
St Erth	d	–	–	–	–	–	–	–	0937	0937
Camborne	d	–	–	–	–	–	–	–	0948	0948
Redruth	d	–	–	–	–	–	0855	–	0955	0955
Truro	d	–	–	–	–	–	0907	–	1007	1007
St Austell	d	–	–	–	–	–	0924	–	1024	1024
Par	d	–	–	–	–	–	0932	–	1032	1032
Bodmin Parkway	d	–	–	–	–	–	0943	–	1043	1043
Liskeard	d	–	–	–	–	–	0955	–	1055	1055
Plymouth	d	–	–	0830	0844	0844	1020	1042	1123	1123
Totnes	d	–	–	0857	0910	0910	1050	1108	1150	1150
Paignton	d	–	–	–	0940	0940	1015	1059	1140	1140
Torquay	d	–	–	–	0946	0946	1021	1105	1145	1145
Newton Abbot	d	–	–	0910	0958	0958	1103	1121	1203	1203
Teignmouth	d	–	–	0916	1004	1004	1041	–	–	–
Dawlish	d	–	–	0921	1009	1009	1046	–	–	–
Exeter St Davids	d	0800	0815	0939	1022	1022	1124	1140	1224	1224
Tiverton Parkway	d	0814	0829	0953	0958	0958	1043	–	1238	1238
Taunton	d	0828	0843	1006	1045	1045	1148	1230	1252	1252
Bristol Temple Meads	a	0902	–	1040	–	–	–	1312	–	1325
Castle Cary	d	–	–	–	–	–	–	–	–	–
Westbury	d	–	0929	–	1132	–	–	–	1338	–
Pewsey	d	–	0945	–	–	–	–	–	–	–
Newbury	a	–	1004	–	–	–	–	–	–	–
Reading	a	1000	1034	1135	1226	1227	1316	1424	1432	1430
Gatwick Airport	a	1131	1231	1331	1431	1431	1511	–	1631	1631
Heathrow Terminal 1	a	1100	1200	1300	1330	1330	1430	–	1600	1530
London Paddington	a	1043	1115	1213	1305	1305	1359	1500	1514	1514

Use the timetable to answer these questions:

(a)   David catches the 0939 at Exeter St Davids. At what time does he arrive in London?

(b)   Stewart arrives in London at 1514. At what time did he leave St Erth?

(c)   Helen wants to travel from Camborne to Plymouth. What is the earliest time she can get there by train?

(d)   Misha arrives in Reading at 1432. At what time did she leave Truro?

7.   Use the following bus timetable to answer these questions:

(a)   What bus should you catch from Glasgow to be at Clydebank by 1:00 p.m?

(b)   You arrive at the bus stop in Tarbet at 1300. At what time could you arrive in Connel?

(c)   If you leave Glasgow at 1000, at what time will you arrive in Oban?

(d)   If you catch the 1233 bus from Anniesland, where will you get off the bus in Dalmally?

GLASGOW	Buchanan Bus Stn	0815	1000	–	1215	1800
Hillhead	Gt Western Rd at Kersland St	0825	1010	–	1225	1810
Gartnavel	Gt Western Rd Bus Stop	0829	1015	–	1229	1814
Anniesland	Cross	0833	1019	–	1233	1818
Drumchapel	Drumry Roundabout	0841	1026	–	1241	1826
Clydebank	Gt Western Rd at Kilbowie Rd	0844	1029	–	1244	1829
Dumbarton	Barloan Toll	0855	1043	–	1255	1840
Balloch	Layby near Roundabout	0900	1048	–	1300	1845
Luss	Bypass	0911	1100	–	1311	1856
Tarbet	Hotel	0921	1111	–	1321	1906
Arrochar	Braeside Stores	0925	–	–	1325	1910
Cairndow	War Memorial	0944	–	–	1344	1928
INVERARAY arr	Front Street	1000	–	–	1405	1945
INVERARAY dep	Front Street	1010	–	–	1415	1955
TYNDRUM arr	Little Chef	–	1200	–	–	–
TYNDRUM dep	Little Chef	–	–	1215	–	–
Dalmally	opp Glen Orchy Hotel	1035	–	–	1440	2020
Dalmally	opp Police Station	–	–	1233	–	–
Taynuilt	Hotel	1054	–	1252	1459	2039
Connel	Bypass at Bridge	1104	–	1304	1509	2049
OBAN	Railway Station	1115	–	1315	1520	2100

8. This timetable gives the times of departures of the ferry between Penzance and St Mary's on the Isles of Scilly, for 1998.

Mondays to Fridays, daily	
6 April to 2 October	Depart Penzance 0915 Depart St Mary's 1630

Saturdays only	
4 April to 2 May 11 July	Depart Penzance 0915 Depart St Mary's 1630
9 May & 16 May 6 June to 4 July 5 Sept to 3 October	Depart Penzance 1100 Depart St Mary's 1500
23 May & 30 May 18 July to 29 August	Depart Penzance 0630 and 1345 Depart St Mary's 0945 and 1700

Sundays only	
30 August	Depart Penzance 0915 Depart St Mary's 1630

Monday, Wednesday, Friday, Saturday	
5 October to 31 October	Depart Penzance 0915 Depart St Mary's 1630

(a) What was the date of the only Sunday in 1998 on which you could catch the ferry?

(b) At what time did the ferry leave Penzance on Saturday 6 June?

(c) At what time did the ferry leave St Mary's on Wednesday 14 October?

(d) Was there a ferry on Thursday 15 October?

(e) On how many days were there *two* return journeys instead of the usual one?

9. The table gives the flight numbers and times of flights to and from the Isles of Scilly from Newquay, Plymouth and Southampton.

To ISLES OF SCILLY			From ISLES OF SCILLY		
Newquay (Flight time 30 mins)					
5Y201	0930	TWTh	5Y200	0830	TWTh
5Y203	1000	M FS	5Y202	0900	M FS
5Y205	1445	M W FS	5Y204	1330	M W FS
5Y207	1745	T Th	5Y206	1630	T Th
Plymouth (Flight time 45 mins)					
5Y301	1335	M W F	5Y300	1220	M W F
Southampton (Flight time 90 mins)					
5Y501	1000	M F	5Y500	0800	M F
M - Mon, T - Tues, W - Wed, Th - Thurs, F - Fri, S - Sat, Su - Sun					

The left hand side of the table gives flights *to* the Isles of Scilly and the right hand side gives flights *from* the Isles of Scilly.

(a) On which days can you fly from Southampton to the Isles of Scilly?

(b) On which day are there no flights from any of these airports to the Isles of Scilly?

(c) If you catch the 1000 from Newquay, at what time do you arrive in the Isles of Scilly?

(d) Khan arrives in the Isles of Scilly at 1130. Where did he fly from?

(e) What is the latest time that you could land in the Isles of Scilly?

10. The following timetable gives details of flights from the Isle of Man to Heathrow:

Isle of Man to London Heathrow

Flight Number	Operation Dates	Days	Routes	Depart - Arrive
JE301	30SEP - 16OCT98	123456-	IOM - LHR	0700 - 0815
JE301	19OCT - 24OCT98	123456-	IOM - LHR	0700 - 0815
JE301	17OCT - 17OCT98	- - - - - 6-	IOM - LHR	0700 - 0815
JE305	30SEP - 23OCT98	12345 - -	IOM - LHR	1440 - 1540
JE307	30SEP - 23OCT98	12345 - 7	IOM - LHR	1755 - 1900
JE309	04OCT - 18OCT98	- - - - - - 7	IOM - LHR	0740 - 0900
JE311	03OCT - 10OCT98	- - - - - 6 -	IOM - LHR	1755 - 1855
JE311	24OCT - 24OCT98	- - - - - 6 -	IOM - LHR	1755 - 1855
JE311	17OCT - 17OCT98	- - - - - 6 -	IOM - LHR	1755 - 1855
JE307	25OCT - 25OCT98	- - - - - - 7	IOM - LHR	1755 - 1900
JE313	25OCT - 25OCT98	- - - - - - 7	IOM - LHR	1040 - 1200

Days
1 = Monday
2 = Tuesday
3 = Wednesday
4 = Thursday
5 = Friday
6 = Saturday
7 = Sunday

(a) What is the flight number of the plane that arrives at Heathrow at 0900, and on which day?

(b) On which day does the 1755 flight have the shortest journey time?

(c) How many flights are there to Heathrow on Sunday 25 October?

(d) What is the *earliest* departure time on Wednesday 21 October?

(e) What is the *latest* arrival time on Saturday 10 October?

14.5 Time Problems in Context

In this section we consider further problems involving time, travel and also rates of pay.

Example 1

The timetable below gives the times of buses from Glasgow to Edinburgh:

GLASGOW	Buchanan Bus Stn	1445	1500	1515	1530	1545
Eurocentral	Gt A8 Interchange	–	–	–	1550	–
Harthill	Service Area	1510	1525	1540	1600	1610
Newbridge East	A8 opp RACAL	1531	1546	1601	1621	1631
Ratho	Sation Road End	1532	1547	1602	1622	1632
Ingliston Showground	West Entrance	1534	1549	1604	1624	1634
Corstorphine	Drum Brae	1538	1553	1608	1628	1638
Corstorphine	Station Road End	1540	1555	1610	1630	1640
Corstorphine	Zoo Park	1542	1557	1612	1632	1642
Murrayfield	Corstorphine Rd, Ice Rink	1545	1600	1615	1635	1645
Edinburgh	Haymarket	1548	1603	1618	1638	1648
Edinburgh	Shandwick Place	1550	1605	1620	1640	1650
EDINBURGH	St Andrew Sq Bus Station	1555	1610	1625	1645	1655

(a) How long does it take for the 1500 from Glasgow to get to Ratho?

(b) How long does it take for the 1545 from Glasgow to get to Edinburgh Haymarket?

(c) How long does it take the 1540 from Harthill to get to Murrayfield?

Solution

(a) The 1500 arrives at Ratho at 1547.

This is 47 minutes later than 1500, so the journey takes 47 minutes.

(b) The journey starts at 1545 and ends at 1648.

From 1545 to 1600 is 15 minutes.

From 1600 to 1648 is 48 minutes.

The total time is 15 + 48 = 63 minutes or 1 hour 3 minutes.

(c) The journey starts at 1540 and ends at 1615.

From 1540 to 1600 is 20 minutes.

From 1600 to 1615 is 15 minutes.

The total time is 20 + 15 = 35 minutes.

Example 2

The table gives the time differences between the UK and some other countries:

Austria	1 hour	ahead
Honduras	6 hours	behind
Samoa	11 hours	ahead
Tanzania	3 hours	ahead

(a)   What time is it in *Austria* when it is 3.00 p.m. in the UK?

(b)   What time is it in *Samoa* when it is 5.00 p.m. in the UK?

(c)   When it is 5.00 p.m. in *Tanzania*, what time is it in the UK?

(d)   If it is 4.00 p.m. in *Honduras*, what time is it in *Tanzania*?

Solution

(a)   In Austria the time is 1 hour ahead of the UK, so it will be 4.00 p.m.

(b)   In Samoa the time is 11 hours ahead of the UK, so it will be 4.00 a.m. the next day.

(c)   In Tanzania the time is 3 hours ahead of the UK, so it will be 2.00 p.m.

(d)   In Honduras the time is 6 hours behind the UK.
        In the UK the time will be 10.00 p.m.
        In Tanzania the time is 3 hours ahead of the UK, so it will be 1.00 a.m.

Exercises

1.   The timetable below gives the times of some buses from Glasgow to Edinburgh:

GLASGOW	Buchanan Bus Stn	1015	1030	1045	1100	1115
Eurocentral	Gt A8 Interchange	–	–	–	–	–
Harthill	Service Area	1040	1055	1110	1125	1140
Newbridge East	A8 opp RACAL	1101	1116	1131	1146	1201
Ratho	Station Road End	1102	1117	1132	1147	1202
Ingliston Showground	West Entrance	1104	1119	1134	1149	1204
Corstorphine	Drum Brae	1108	1123	1138	1153	1208
Corstorphine	Station Road End	1110	1125	1140	1155	1210
Corstorphine	Zoo Park	1112	1127	1142	1157	1212
Murrayfield	Corstorphine Rd, Ice Rink	1115	1130	1145	1200	1215
Edinburgh	Haymarket	1118	1133	1148	1203	1218
Edinburgh	Shandwick Place	1120	1135	1150	1205	1220
EDINBURGH	St Andrew Sq Bus Station	1125	1140	1155	1210	1225

Use the timetable to answer these questions:

(a)   You catch the 1030 from Glasgow. How long will it take to get to Harthill?

(b)   You catch the 1100 from Glasgow. How long does it take to get to Ratho?

(c)   You catch the bus at Harthill and arrive in Edinburgh at 1225. How long did the journey take?

(d)   You arrive in Edinburgh at 1210, having travelled from Harthill. How long did the journey take?

(e)   Do all the buses take the same time to get from Glasgow to Edinburgh?

2.   The timetable below is for the Eurostar train that travels from Disneyland Paris (France) to Waterloo:

Disneyland Paris to Waterloo	
Disneyland Paris	1935
Ashford International	2037
Waterloo International	2139

How long is the journey time from Disneyland to:

(a)   Ashford International,

(b)   Waterloo International?

(Note that France is 1 hour ahead of UK time.)

3.   The timetable below is for the North York Moors Railway.

Grosmont dep.	0950	1050	1150	1250	1350	1450	1550	1650
Goatland arr.	1005	1105	1205	1305	1405	1505	1605	1705
Goatland dep.	1010	1110	1210	1310	1410	1510	1610	1710
Newtondale	1023	1123	1223	1323	1423	1523	1623	1723
Levisham arr.	1036	1136	1236	1336	1436	1536	1636	1736
Levisham dep.	1040	1140	1240	1340	1440	1540	1640	1740
Pickering arr.	1100	1200	1300	1400	1500	1600	1700	1800

(a)   Do all the journeys take the same time?

(b)   For how long do the trains stay at Goathland?

(c)   How long does it take to get from Grosmont to Newtondale?

(d)   How long does it take to get from Grosmont to Levisham?

(e)   For how long do the trains stay at Levisham?

4. Use the timetable below to answer the questions which follow:

Saturdays								
London Paddington	d	1135	1145	1235	1335	1535	1635	1700
Reading	d	1200	1210	1300	1400	1605	1705	1730
Newbury	d	–	–	–	–	–	1721	–
Pewsey	d	–	–	–	–	–	1740	1855
Westbury	d	–	1256	1346	1445	1650	1802	–
Castle Cary	d	–	1313	–	1503	–	1819	–
Bristol Temple Meads	d	–	–	–	–	–	–	–
Taunton	d	–	1335	1423	1529	1726	1841	–
Tiverton Parkway	d	–	1348	1502	1542	1738	1853	–
Exeter St Davids	d	1337	1404	1450	1600	1754	1909	–
Dawlish	d	1403	1423	1537	1646	1829	1921	–
Teignmouth	d	1409	1429	1543	1651	1834	1926	–
Newton Abbot	d	1415	1437	1512	1620	1814	1933	–
Torquay	a	1426	1448	1616	1711	1835	1955	–
Paignton	a	1433	1500	1623	1717	1841	2000	–
Totnes	d	–	1454	1526	1634	1829	1947	–
Plymouth	d	1436	1523	1558	1705	1902	2020	–
Liskeard	d	1502	1552	1628	1729	1926	–	–
Bodmin Parkway	d	1514	1604	1638	1741	1941	–	–
Par	d	–	1615	1652	1847	1953	–	–
St Austell	d	1530	1623	1658	1757	2001	–	–
Truro	d	1548	1641	1716	1815	2019	–	–
Redruth	d	1600	1653	1731	1827	2031	–	–
Camborne	d	–	1700	1738	1834	2038	–	–
St Erth	d	1614	1711	1751	1846	2051	–	–
Penzance	a	1630	1722	1805	1900	2107	–	–

(a) How long does it take for the 1635 from London Paddington to get to Plymouth?

(b) Adrian catches a train at 2:00 pm at Reading. How long does it take him to get to Truro?

(c) Sam catches the last train from Totnes to Penzance. How long does his journey take?

(d) Clare catches the 1445 from Westbury to Plymouth. At what time does she arrive in Plymouth?

(e) Which train has the shortest journey time from London to Penzance?

5. The timetable below is for the overnight ski train from London to the French Alps:

London Waterloo International	(Friday) depart	1957
Ashford International	(Friday) depart	2107
Moûtiers	(Saturday) arrive	0552
Aime la Plagne	(Saturday) arrive	0625
Bourg-St-Maurice	(Saturday) arrive	0645

How long does it take to travel:

(a) from Waterloo to Moûtiers,

(b) from Ashford to Aime la Plagne,

(c) from Waterloo to Bourg-St-Maurice?

6. Use the information given in Example 2 to answer these questions:

(a) What will be the time in Honduras when it is 7:00 am in the UK?

(b) What will be the time in the UK when it is 7:00 pm in Honduras?

(c) What is the time in Tanzania when it is 10:00 pm in the UK?

(d) What is the time in the UK when it is 10:00 pm in Samoa?

7. The flight from London to Stockholm (Sweden) takes $2\frac{1}{2}$ hours. The time in Sweden is 1 hour ahead of the UK.

(a) If you leave London at 1000, what will be the local time when you land at Stockholm?

(b) If you leave Stockholm at 1745, what will be the local time when you land in London?

8. A flight leaves Kuala Lumpur at 1100 and lands in London at 1710. The time in Kuala Lumpur is 8 hours ahead of the time in London. How long does the flight take?

9. Shainee earns £4 per hour on weekdays, £4.50 per hour on Saturdays and £6 per hour on Sundays.

The table below lists the hours he worked on each day of one week:

Day	No. hours worked
Monday	4
Tuesday	2
Wednesday	8
Thursday	10
Friday	3
Saturday	5
Sunday	2

How much money did Shainee earn that week?

10. Ben earns £5 per hour for the first 40 hours he works and £7.50 per hour for any hours of overtime. One week he earned £290. How many hours overtime did he work?

15 Negative Numbers

15.1 Addition and Subtraction

In this section we consider how to add and subtract when working with negative numbers. This is done using a number line.

To *add a positive number*, move to the *right* on a number line.

To *add a negative number*, move to the *left* on a number line.

Example 1

Calculate:

(a) $-3 + 8$ (b) $4 + (-2)$

(c) $-8 + 5$ (d) $-1 + (-3)$

Solution

(a) $-3 + 8$

Start at -3 and move 8 to the right:

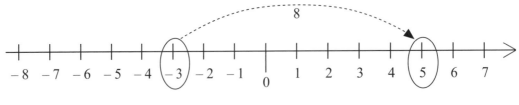

So, $-3 + 8 = 5$.

(b) $4 + (-2)$

Start at 4 and move 2 to the left:

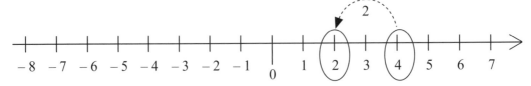

So, $4 + (-2) = 2$.

(c)　　$-8 + 5$

Start at -8 and move 5 to the right:

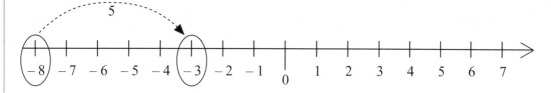

So,　$-8 + 5 = -3$.

(d)　　$-1 + (-3)$

Start at -1 and move 3 to the left:

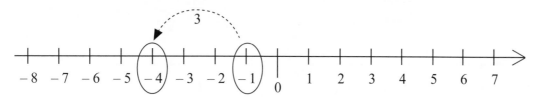

So,　$-1 + (-3) = -4$.

Subtraction is the *inverse* (or opposite) of addition, so

> To *subtract a positive number*, move to the *left* on a number line.
>
> To *subtract a negative number*, move to the *right* on a number line.

Example 2

Calculate:

(a)　　$5 - 7$　　　　　　　　(b)　　$-2 - 3$

(c)　　$4 - (-2)$　　　　　　(d)　　$-5 - (-3)$

Solution

(a) $5 - 7$

     Start at 5 and move 7 to the left:

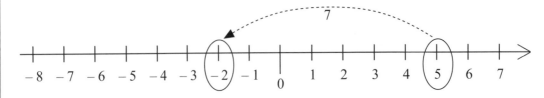

     So, $5 - 7 = -2$.

(b) $-2 - 3$

     Start at -2 and move 3 to the left:

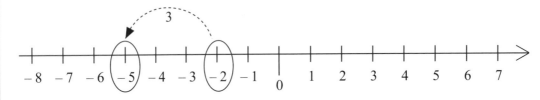

     So, $-2 - 3 = -5$.

(c) $4 - (-2)$

     Start at 4 and move 2 to the right:

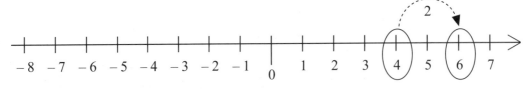

     So, $4 - (-2) = 6$.

(d) $-5 - (-3)$

     Start at -5 and move 3 to the right:

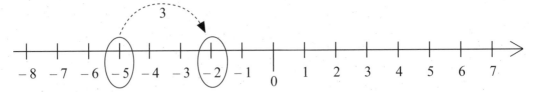

     So, $5 - (-3) = -2$.

Exercises

1. Use a number line to work out the following calculations:

   (a) $-4 + 6$ (b) $-5 + 8$ (c) $-1 + 3$

   (d) $-4 + 7$ (e) $2 + (-3)$ (f) $-1 + (-4)$

   (g) $-2 + (-3)$ (h) $-6 + 6$ (i) $-7 + 4$

   (j) $-6 + 2$ (k) $-7 + 2$ (l) $5 + (-5)$

2. Use a number line to calculate:

   (a) $4 - 6$ (b) $5 - 7$ (c) $2 - 4$

   (d) $-1 - 1$ (e) $-3 - 2$ (f) $-4 - (-1)$

   (g) $3 - (-4)$ (h) $5 - (-6)$ (i) $8 - 12$

   (j) $-5 - (-1)$ (k) $4 - 9$ (l) $-4 - (-4)$

3. Write down the two possible sums that could be shown by each number line below:

   (a)

   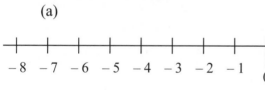
   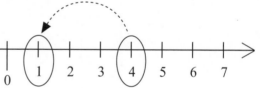

   (b)

   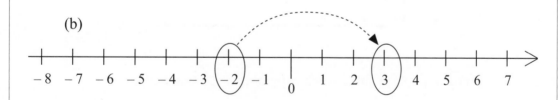

   (c)

   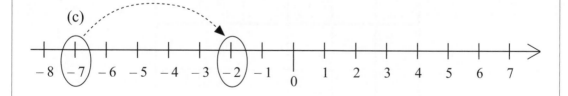

   (d)

   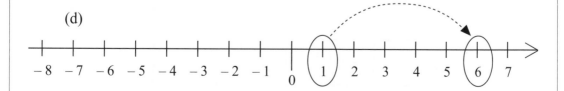

(e)

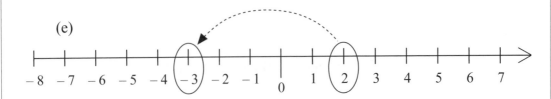

(f)

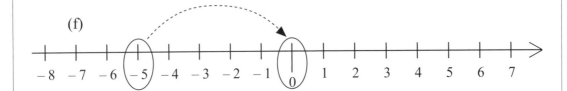

(g)

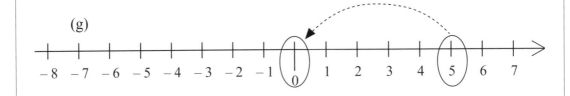

4. Copy and complete this addition table:

+	−4	−2	0	2	4
−3					
−1					
1					
3					

5. Fill in the missing numbers on a copy of this addition table:

+		1		3	
−5	−5				−1
		−3			
				0	
	−2		0		

6. Copy these equations and fill in the missing numbers:

   (a) $4 + \ldots = 1$

   (b) $3 - \ldots = -6$

   (c) $-6 + \ldots = -7$

   (d) $\ldots + 7 = 2$

   (e) $\ldots - 7 = -8$

   (f) $4 - \ldots = 7$

7. Write down the next 5 terms in each sequence:

   (a)   10, 8, 6, 4, ...

   (b)   −10, −7, −4, −1, ...

   (c)   19, 14, 9, 4, ...

   (d)   −1, −3, −5, −7, ...

   (e)   −20, −16, −12, −8, ...

   (f)   −5, −10, −15, −20 ...

   (g)   18, 15, 12, 9, ...

   (h)   −16, −12, −8, −4, ...

8. Overnight, the temperature dropped from $5\,°C$ to $-14\,°C$. By how many degrees did the temperature fall?

9. One day the level of the water in a river was 30 cm *above* its average level. One week later it was 12 cm *below* its average level. How far did the water level drop in the week?

10. A chest of treasure was hidden in the year 64 BC and found in 284 AD. For how long was the chest hidden?

15.2 Multiplication and Division

In this section we look at how to multiply and divide negative numbers.

Example 1

(a) Calculate
$$(-2) + (-2) + (-2) + (-2) + (-2).$$

(b) Fill in the missing numbers:
$$(-2) + (-2) + (-2) + (-2) + (-2) = \ldots \times (-2) = \ldots$$

Solution

(a) $(-2) + (-2) + (-2) + (-2) + (-2) = -10$

(b) $(-2) + (-2) + (-2) + (-2) + (-2) = 5 \times (-2) = -10$

> In Example 1 we see that
>
> *a positive number multiplied by*
> *a negative number gives a negative answer.*
>
> This table shows what happens to the sign of the answer when positive and negative numbers are *multiplied*:
>
> | $\times$ | $+$ | $-$ |
> |:---:|:---:|:---:|
> | $+$ | $+$ | $-$ |
> | $-$ | $-$ | $+$ |
>
> The same table can be used for *division* of positive and negative numbers.

Example 2

Work out the following:

(a) $5 \times (-7)$ (b) $(-8) \times (-10)$

(c) $(-42) \div 6$ (d) $(-88) \div (-8)$

Solution

(a)   First calculate $5 \times 7 = 35$.

      As a positive number is multiplied by a negative number, the answer will be negative:
$$5 \times (-7) = -35$$

(b)   First calculate $8 \times 10 = 80$.

      Here a negative number is multiplied by a negative number, so the answer will be positive:
$$(-8) \times (-10) = 80$$

(c)   First calculate $42 \div 6 = 7$.

      As a negative number is divided by a positive number, the answer will be negative:
$$(-42) \div 6 = -7$$

(c)   First calculate $88 \div 8 = 11$.

As a negative number is divided by a negative number, the answer will be positive:

$$(-88) \div (-8) = 11$$

Exercises

1.   Calculate:

(a) $(-7) \times 2$ (b) $(-4) \times 8$ (c) $(-2) \times (-5)$

(d) $(-6) \times (-3)$ (e) $(-3) \times 7$ (f) $(-10) \times (-4)$

(g) 8×4 (h) $3 \times (-6)$ (i) $(-7) \times (-2)$

(j) $(-4) \times (-5)$ (k) $(-7) \times 0$ (l) $8 \times (-5)$

2.   Calculate:

(a) $(-10) \div (-2)$ (b) $(-15) \div 5$

(c) $18 \div (-3)$ (d) $14 \div (-7)$

(e) $(-21) \div (-3)$ (f) $(-45) \div 9$

(g) $50 \div (-5)$ (h) $(-100) \div (-4)$

(i) $80 \div (-2)$ (j) $26 \div (-13)$

(k) $(-70) \div (-7)$ (l) $(-42) \div 7$

3.   Copy and complete these multiplication tables:

(a)

×	1	2	3	4
−1				
−2				
−3				
−4				

(b)

×	1	0	−1	−2	−3
−4					
−2					
0					
1					

15.2

4. Copy and complete these multiplication tables:

(a)

×		−1	
2			
	−2	2	
−3			−9

(b)

×	−2		
	10		
−2		6	
3			−12

5. Copy these calculations, filling in the missing numbers:

(a) $\ldots\ldots \times 5 = -20$

(b) $(-80) \div \ldots\ldots = 4$

(c) $16 \times \ldots\ldots = -32$

(d) $(-4) \times \ldots\ldots = 32$

(e) $\ldots\ldots \times (-3) = 12$

(f) $40 \div \ldots\ldots = -8$

(g) $-8 \times \ldots\ldots = 48$

(h) $-32 \div \ldots\ldots = 4$

(i) $15 \times \ldots\ldots = -60$

(j) $100 \div \ldots\ldots = -25$

6. Write down the next 3 terms in each sequence:

(a) $1, \ -2, \ 4, \ -8, \ 16, \ \ldots$

(b) $-1, \ 2, \ -4, \ 8, \ -16, \ \ldots$

(c) $1, \ -10, \ 100, \ -1000, \ \ldots$

(d) $1, \ -3, \ 9, \ -27, \ \ldots$

(e) $-1, \ 5, \ -25, \ 125, \ \ldots$

For each sequence, describe the rule that is used to calculate the next term.

7. Make 2 copies of this multiplication table and fill in the missing numbers in 2 different ways:

×				
	1			
		4		
			9	
				25

8.   Calculate:

(a) $3 \times (-8) \times (-4)$ (b) $(-4) \times (-8) \times (-2)$

(c) $(-2) \times (-2) \times 2$ (d) $4 \times (-7) \times 2$

(e) $(-2) \times 8 \times (-4)$ (f) $(-6) \times (-2) \times (-1)$

9.   Calculate:

(a) $\dfrac{(-3) \times (-4)}{(-2)}$ (b) $\dfrac{5 \times (-6)}{(-2)}$

(c) $\dfrac{(-7) \times (-5) \times (-2)}{5}$ (d) $\dfrac{8 \times (-9) \times 6}{(-2) \times (-3)}$

(e) $\dfrac{(-6) \times (-4)}{2}$ (f) $\dfrac{(-4) \times (-7) \times 3}{(-12)}$

10.   Calculate:

(a) $(-6 + 10) \div (-2)$ (b) $(12 - 24) \div (-2)$

(c) $(6 + (-8)) \times (4 - 7)$ (d) $((-2) + 8) \times ((-4) + 2)$

(e) $((-4) \times 2) + (6 \times (-9))$ (f) $(8 \times (-2)) - ((-4) \times 8)$

11.   Calculate:

(a) $(-6) \times (-3) + (-4)$ (b) $(-5) \times 4 - (-3)$

(c) $(-8) \times (-7) - 8 \times 7$ (d) $(-11) \times 4 + (-8) \times (-3)$

16 | Algebra: Linear Equations

16.1 | Fundamental Algebraic Skills

This section looks at some fundamental algebraic skills by examining codes and how to use formulae.

Example 1

Use this code wheel, which codes A on the outer ring as Y on the inner ring, to:

(a) code the word M A T H S,

(b) decode Q M L G A.

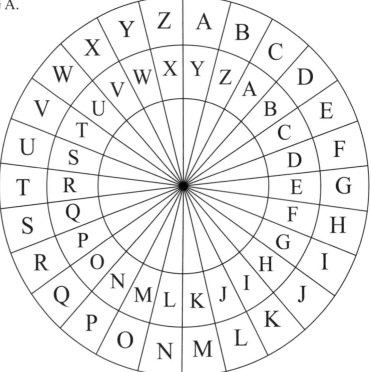

Solution

(a) Look for M on the outside circle of letters; this is coded as K which is the letter on the inside circle. Coding the other letters in the same way gives:

$$
\begin{array}{ccccc}
M & A & T & H & S \\
\downarrow & \downarrow & \downarrow & \downarrow & \downarrow \\
K & Y & R & F & Q
\end{array}
$$

(b) Look for Q on the inside circle. This decodes as S, which is the letter on the outside circle. Decoding the other letters in the same way gives:

$$
\begin{array}{ccccc}
Q & M & L & G & A \\
\downarrow & \downarrow & \downarrow & \downarrow & \downarrow \\
S & O & N & I & C
\end{array}
$$

Example 2

If $a = 4$, $b = 7$ and $c = 3$, calculate:

(a) $6 + b$ (b) $2a + b$ (c) ab (d) $a(b - c)$

Solution

(a) $\begin{aligned} 6 + b &= 6 + 7 \\ &= 13 \end{aligned}$

(b) $\begin{aligned} 2a + b &= 2 \times 4 + 7 \\ &= 8 + 7 \\ &= 15 \end{aligned}$ since $\boxed{2a = 2 \times a}$

(c) $\begin{aligned} ab &= 4 \times 7 \\ &= 28 \end{aligned}$ since $\boxed{ab = a \times b}$

(d) $\begin{aligned} a(b - c) &= 4 \times (7 - 3) \\ &= 4 \times 4 \\ &= 16 \end{aligned}$ since $\boxed{a(b - c) = a \times (b - c)}$

Example 3

Simplify where possible:

(a) $2x + 4x$ (b) $5p + 7q - 3p + 2q$

(c) $y + 8y - 5y$ (d) $3t + 4s$

Solution

(a) $\begin{aligned} 2x + 4x &= 2 \times x + 4 \times x \\ &= (x + x) + (x + x + x + x) \\ &= 6 \times x \\ &= 6x \end{aligned}$

(b) $\begin{aligned} 5p + 7q - 3p + 2q &= 5p - 3p + 7q + 2q \\ &= (5 - 3)p + (7 + 2)q \\ &= 2p + 9q \end{aligned}$

(c) $y + 8y - 5y = 1y + 8y - 5y$

$$= (1 + 8 - 5)y$$

$$= 4y$$

(d) $3t + 4s$ cannot be simplified.

Example 4

Write down formulae for the area and perimeter of this rectangle:

Solution

Area $= x \times y$ Perimeter $= x + y + x + y$

$\quad = xy$ $= 2x + 2y$

Exercises

1. Use the code wheel of Example 1 to:

    (a) code this message,

        M E E T   M E   A T   H O M E

    (b) decode this message,

        M T C P   R M   W M S

2. Use the code wheel opposite to:

    (a) code

        G O N E   F I S H I N G,

    (b) decode

        T U S T   R U H Q

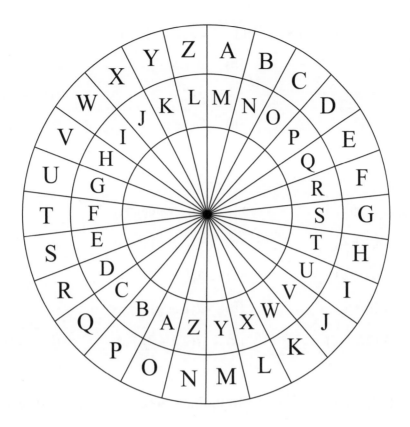

3.   Laura used a code wheel similar to the one above, but with the outer ring of letters rotated. She used her code wheel to code

	S	E	V	E	N		U	P
as	↓	↓	↓	↓	↓		↓	↓
	V	H	Y	H	Q		X	S

(a)   Draw the code wheel that she used.

(b)   Use the code wheel to decode:

G D Q J H U   D K H D G

4.   If $a = 2$, $b = 6$, $c = 10$ and $d = 3$, calculate:

(a) $a + b$ (b) $c - b$ (c) $d + 7$

(d) $3a + d$ (e) $4a$ (f) ad

(g) $3b$ (h) $2c$ (i) $3c - b$

(j) $6a + b$ (k) $3a + 2b$ (l) $4a - d$

5.   If $a = 3$, $b = -1$, $c = 2$ and $d = -4$, calculate:

   (a) $a - b$ (b) $a + d$ (c) $b + d$

   (d) $b - d$ (e) $3d$ (f) $a + b$

   (g) $c - d$ (h) $2c + d$ (i) $3a - d$

   (j) $2d + 3c$ (k) $4a - 2d$ (l) $5a + 3d$

6.   If $a = 7$, $b = 5$, $c = -3$ and $d = 4$, calculate:

   (a) $2(a + b)$ (b) $4(a - b)$ (c) $6(a - d)$

   (d) $2(a + c)$ (e) $5(b - c)$ (f) $5(d - c)$

   (g) $a(b + c)$ (h) $d(b + a)$ (i) $c(b - a)$

   (j) $a(2b - c)$ (k) $d(2a - 3b)$ (l) $c(d - 2)$

7.   Use the formula $s = \dfrac{1}{2}(u + v)t$ to find s, when $u = 10$, $v = 20$ and $t = 4$.

8.   Use the formula $v = u + at$ to find v, if $u = 20$, $a = -2$ and $t = 7$.

9.   Simplify, where possible:

   (a) $2a + 3a$ (b) $5b + 8b$

   (c) $6c - 4c$ (d) $5d + 4d + 7d$

   (e) $6e + 9e - 5e$ (f) $8f + 6f - 13f$

   (g) $9g + 7g - 8g - 2g - 6g$ (h) $5p + 2h$

   (i) $3a + 4b - 2a$ (j) $6x + 3y - 2x - y$

   (k) $8t - 6t + 7s - 2s$

   (l) $11m + 3n - 5p + 2q - 2n + 9q - 8m + 14p$

10. Write down formulae for the perimeter of each of these shapes:

   (a) 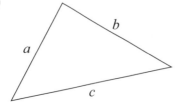   (b)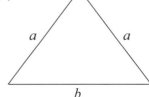

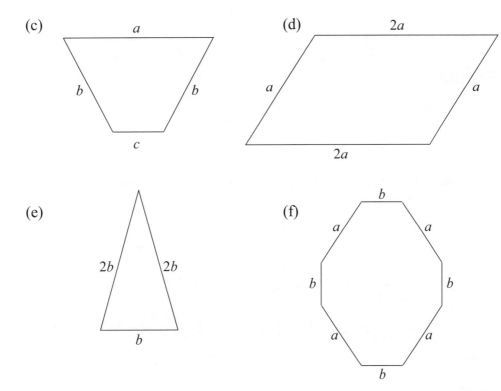

11. Sam asks her friend to think of a number, multiply it by 2 and then add 5. If the number her friend starts with is x, write down a formula for the number her friend gets.

12. A removal firm makes a fixed charge of £50, plus £2 for every mile travelled. Write down the formula for the cost of a removal when travelling x miles.

13. A taxi driver charges passengers £1, plus 50p per mile. Write down a formula for the cost of travelling x miles.

16.2 Function Machines

In this section we look at how to find the input and output of function machines, building on the work on number machines in Book Y7A.

INPUT ⟶ FUNCTION MACHINE ⟼ OUTPUT

Example 1

Calculate the output of each of these function machines:

(a) $4 \longrightarrow \boxed{\times 5} \longmapsto ?$

(b) $5 \longrightarrow \boxed{\times 2} \longmapsto \boxed{-1} \longrightarrow ?$

(c) $-3 \longrightarrow \boxed{+8} \longrightarrow \boxed{\times 7} \longrightarrow ?$

Solution

(a)   The input is simply multiplied by 5 to give 20:

$$4 \longrightarrow \boxed{\times 5} \longrightarrow 20$$

(b)   The input is multiplied by 2 to give 10, and then 1 is subtracted from this to give 9:

$$5 \longrightarrow \boxed{\times 2} \xrightarrow{\ 10\ } \boxed{-1} \longrightarrow 9$$

(c)   Firstly, 8 is added to the input to give 5, and this is then multiplied by 7 to give 35:

$$-3 \longrightarrow \boxed{+8} \xrightarrow{\ 5\ } \boxed{\times 7} \longrightarrow 35$$

Example 2

Calculate the input for each of these function machines:

(a) $? \longrightarrow \boxed{\times 4} \longrightarrow 8$

(b) $? \longrightarrow \boxed{+2} \longrightarrow \boxed{\times 5} \longrightarrow 25$

(c) $? \longrightarrow \boxed{-5} \longrightarrow \boxed{\times 3} \longrightarrow 6$

Solution

The missing inputs can be found by reversing the machines and using the inverse (i.e. opposite) operations in each machine:

(a) $? \longrightarrow \boxed{\times 4} \longrightarrow 8$

$$2 \longleftarrow \boxed{\div 4} \longleftarrow 8$$

(b) $? \longrightarrow \boxed{+2} \longrightarrow \boxed{\times 5} \longrightarrow 25$

$$3 \longleftarrow \boxed{-2} \xleftarrow{\ 5\ } \boxed{\div 5} \longleftarrow 25$$

(c) $? \longrightarrow \boxed{-5} \longrightarrow \boxed{\times 3} \longrightarrow 6$

$$7 \longleftarrow \boxed{+5} \xleftarrow{\ 2\ } \boxed{\div 3} \longleftarrow 6$$

Note that:

Operation	Inverse Operation
+	−
−	+
×	÷
÷	×

Exercises

1. What is the output of each of these function machines:

   (a)   4 ⟶ + 6 ⟶ ?

   (b)   3 ⟶ × 10 ⟶ ?

   (c)   10 ⟶ − 7 ⟶ ?

   (d)   14 ⟶ ÷ 2 ⟶ ?

   (e)   21 ⟶ ÷ 3 ⟶ ?

   (f)   100 ⟶ × 5 ⟶ ?

2. What is the output of each of these function machines:

   (a)   3 ⟶ × 4 ⟶ − 7 ⟶ ?

   (b)   10 ⟶ − 8 ⟶ × 7 ⟶ ?

   (c)   8 ⟶ − 5 ⟶ × 5 ⟶ ?

   (d)   −2 ⟶ × 6 ⟶ + 20 ⟶ ?

   (e)   7 ⟶ + 2 ⟶ ÷ 3 ⟶ ?

   (f)   −5 ⟶ + 8 ⟶ × 9 ⟶ ?

3.   What is the output of each of these function machines:

   (a)   ? ⟶ $\times 5$ ⟶ 30   (b)   ? ⟶ $+ 8$ ⟶ 12

   (c)   ? ⟶ $- 9$ ⟶ 11   (d)   ? ⟶ $\div 4$ ⟶ 5

   (e)   ? ⟶ $+ 12$ ⟶ 21   (f)   ? ⟶ $\times 7$ ⟶ 42

4.   What is the input of each of these *double function* machines:

   (a)   ? ⟶ $+ 1$ ⟶ $\times 4$ ⟶ 12

   (b)   ? ⟶ $+ 7$ ⟶ $\div 6$ ⟶ 4

   (c)   ? ⟶ $\times 4$ ⟶ $+ 9$ ⟶ 37

   (d)   ? ⟶ $\times 9$ ⟶ $- 20$ ⟶ 34

   (e)   ? ⟶ $\div 6$ ⟶ $- 1$ ⟶ 7

   (f)   ? ⟶ $- 6$ ⟶ $\div 7$ ⟶ 9

   (g)   ? ⟶ $+ 8$ ⟶ $\times 4$ ⟶ 24

   (h)   ? ⟶ $\times 2$ ⟶ $+ 7$ ⟶ -3

5.   Here is a *triple function* machine:

   Input ⟶ $\times 7$ ⟶ $- 5$ ⟶ $\div 2$ ⟶ Output

   (a)   What is the *output* if the input is 8.

   (b)   What is the *input* if the output is 22.

   (c)   What is the *input* if the output is -13.

6.   A number is multiplied by 10, and then 6 is added to get 36.
        What was the number?

7.   Karen asks her teacher, Miss Sharp, how old she is. Miss Sharp replies that
        if you double her age, add 7 and then divide by 3, you get 21. How old is
        Miss Sharp?

8. Sally is given her pocket money. She puts half in the bank and then spends £3 in one shop and £2.50 in another shop. She goes home with £1.25. How much pocket money was she given?

9. A bus has its maximum number of passengers when it leaves the bus station. At the first stop, half of the passengers get off. At the next stop 7 people get on and at the next stop 16 people get off. There are now 17 people on the bus. How many passengers were on the bus when it left the bus station?

10. Prakesh buys a tomato plant. In the first week it doubles its height. In the second week it grows 8 cm. In the third week it grows 5 cm. What was the height of the plant when Prakesh bought it if it is now 35 cm in height?

16.3　Linear Equations

An *equation* is a statement, such as $3x + 2 = 17$, which contains an unknown number, in this case, x. The aim of this section is to show how to find the unknown number, x.

All equations contain an 'equals' sign.

To solve the equation, you need to reorganise it so that the unknown value is by itself on one side of the equation. This is done by performing operations on the equation. When you do this, in order to keep the equality of the sides, you must remember that

> *whatever you do to one side of an equation, you must also do the same to the other side*

Example 1

Solve these equations:

(a)　$x + 2 = 8$　　　　(b)　$x - 4 = 3$　　　　(c)　$3x = 12$

(d)　$\dfrac{x}{2} = 7$　　　　(e)　$2x + 5 = 11$　　　　(f)　$3 - 2x = 7$

Solution

(a)　To solve this equation, subtract 2 from each side of the equation:

$$x + 2 = 8$$
$$x + 2 - 2 = 8 - 2$$
$$x = 6$$

16.3

(b) To solve this equation, add 4 to both sides of the equation:

$$x - 4 = 3$$
$$x - 4 + 4 = 3 + 4$$
$$x = 7$$

(c) To solve this equation, divide both sides of the equation by 3:

$$3x = 12$$
$$\frac{3x}{3} = \frac{12}{3}$$
$$x = 4$$

(d) To solve this equation, multiply both sides of the equation by 2:

$$\frac{x}{2} = 7$$
$$2 \times \frac{x}{2} = 2 \times 7$$
$$x = 14$$

(e) This equation must be solved in 2 stages.
First, subtract 5 from both sides:

$$2x + 5 = 11$$
$$2x + 5 - 5 = 11 - 5$$
$$2x = 6$$

Then, divide both sides of the equation by 2:

$$\frac{2x}{2} = \frac{6}{2}$$
$$x = 3$$

(f) First, subtract 3 from both sides:

$$3 - 2x = 7$$
$$3 - 2x - 3 = 7 - 3$$
$$-2x = 4$$

Then divide both sides by (-2):

$$\frac{-2x}{-2} = \frac{4}{-2}$$
$$x = -2$$

Example 2

Solve these equations:

(a) $3x + 2 = 4x - 3$

(b) $2x + 7 = 8x - 11$

Solution

These equations contain x on both sides. The first step is to change them so that x is on only *one* side of the equation. Choose the side which has the most x; here, the right hand side.

(a)   Subtract $3x$ from both sides of the equation:

$$3x + 2 = 4x - 3$$

$$3x + 2 - 3x = 4x - 3 - 3x$$

$$2 = x - 3$$

Then add 3 to both sides of the equation:

$$2 = x - 3$$

$$2 + 3 = x - 3 + 3$$

$$5 = x$$

so $x = 5$

Note: *it is conventional to give the answer with the unknown value, x, on the left hand side, and its value on the right hand side.*

(b)   First, subtract $2x$ from both sides of the equation:

$$2x + 7 = 8x - 11$$

$$2x + 7 - 2x = 8x - 11 - 2x$$

$$7 = 6x - 11$$

Next, add 11 to both sides of the equation:

$$7 + 11 = 6x - 11 + 11$$

$$18 = 6x$$

Then divide both sides by 6:

$$\frac{18}{6} = \frac{6x}{6}$$

$$3 = x$$

so $x = 3$

Example 3

You ask a friend to think of a number. He then multiplies it by 5 and subtracts 7. He gets the answer 43.

(a)   Use this information to write down an equation for x, the unknown number.

(b)   Solve your equation for x.

Solution

(a)   As x = number your friend thought of, then

$$x \longrightarrow \boxed{\times 5} \xrightarrow{5x} \boxed{-7} \longrightarrow 5x - 7$$

So $5x - 7 = 43$

(b)   First, add 7 to both sides of the equation to give

$$5x = 50$$

Then divide both sides by 5 to give

$$x = 10$$

and this is the number that your friend thought of.

Exercises

1.   Solve these equations:

(a) $x + 2 = 8$ (b) $x + 5 = 11$ (c) $x - 6 = 2$

(d) $x - 4 = 3$ (e) $2x = 18$ (f) $3x = 24$

(g) $\dfrac{x}{6} = 4$ (h) $\dfrac{x}{5} = 9$ (i) $6x = 54$

(j) $x + 12 = 10$ (k) $x + 5 = 3$ (l) $x - 22 = -4$

(m) $\dfrac{x}{7} = -2$ (n) $10x = 0$ (o) $\dfrac{x}{2} + 4 = 5$

2.   Solve these equations:

(a) $2x + 4 = 14$ (b) $3x + 7 = 25$ (c) $4x + 2 = 22$

(d) $6x - 4 = 26$ (e) $5x - 3 = 32$ (f) $11x - 4 = 29$

(g) $3x + 4 = 25$ (h) $5x - 8 = 37$ (i) $6x + 7 = 31$

(j) $3x + 11 = 5$ (k) $6x + 2 = -10$ (l) $7x + 44 = 2$

3. Solve these equations, giving your answers as fractions or mixed numbers:

   (a) $3x = 4$ (b) $5x = 7$ (c) $2x + 8 = 13$

   (d) $8x + 2 = 5$ (e) $2x + 6 = 9$ (f) $4x - 7 = 10$

4. The perimeter of this triangle is 31 cm.

   Use this information to write down an equation for x and solve it to find x.

   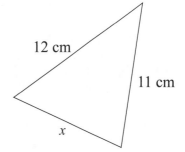

5. (a) Write down an expression for the length of the perimeter of this rectangle:

   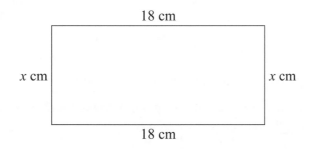

   (b) Find x if the perimeter length is 48 cm.

   (c) Find x if the perimeter length is 45 cm.

6. Tom asks each of his friends to think of their age, double it and then take away 10.

   Here are the answers he is given:

Ben	Ian	Adam	Sergio
8	10	14	11

   (a) Using x to represent Ben's age, write down an equation for x and solve it to find Ben's age.

   (b) Write down and solve equations to find the ages of Ian, Adam and Sergio.

7. The perimeter of this octagon is 9.6 cm.

   Write down an equation and solve it to find x.

   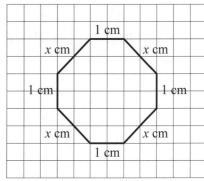

8.   Solve these equations:

(a) $x + 2 = 2x - 1$ (b) $8x - 1 = 4x + 11$

(c) $5x + 2 = 6x - 4$ (d) $11x - 4 = 2x + 23$

(e) $5x + 1 = 6x - 8$ (f) $3x + 2 + 5x = x + 44$

(g) $6x + 2 - 2x = x + 23$ (h) $2x - 3 = 6x + x - 58$

(i) $3x + 2 = x - 8$ (j) $4x - 2 = 2x - 8$

(k) $3x + 82 = 10x + 12$ (l) $6x - 10 = 2x - 14$

9.   The diagram below shows three angles on a straight line:

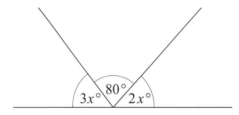

(a)   Write down an equation and use it to find x.

(b)   Write down the sizes of the two unknown angles and check that the three angles shown add up to $180°$.

10.   Use an equation to find the sizes of the unknown angles in this triangle:

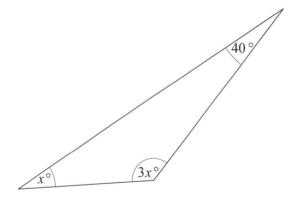

11.   Karen thinks of a number, multiplies it by 3 and then adds 10. Her answer is 11 more than the number she thought of. If x is her original number, write down an equation and solve it to find x.

17 Arithmetic: Decimals, Fractions and Percentages

17.1 Conversion: Decimals into Fractions

In this section we revise ideas of decimals and work on writing decimals as fractions.

Recall that the number

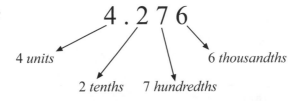

means
      4 *units*   6 *thousandths*

          2 *tenths*   7 *hundredths*

The table below shows how to write the fractions you need to know in order to write decimals as fractions:

Decimal	Words	Fraction
0.1	1 tenth	$\dfrac{1}{10}$
0.01	1 hundredth	$\dfrac{1}{100}$
0.001	1 thousandth	$\dfrac{1}{1000}$

Example 1

Write these numbers in order, with the smallest first:

$$0.7, \quad 0.17, \quad 0.77, \quad 0.71, \quad 0.701, \quad 0.107$$

Solution

Note: It is, perhaps, easier to see this if we first write *all* the numbers to 3 decimal places,

    i.e. 0.700, 0.170, 0.770, 0.710, 0.701, 0.107

The required order is:

    0.107, 0.17, 0.7, 0.701, 0.71, 0.77

Example 2

Write these numbers as fractions, where possible giving them in their simplest form:

(a)	0.7	(b)	0.09	(c)	0.004
(d)	0.47	(e)	0.132	(f)	1.75

Solution

(a) $0.7 = \dfrac{7}{10}$

(b) $0.09 = \dfrac{9}{100}$

(c) $0.004 = \dfrac{4}{1000} = \dfrac{1}{250}$

(d) $0.47 = \dfrac{47}{100}$

(e) $0.132 = \dfrac{132}{1000} = \dfrac{33}{250}$

(f) $1.75 = \dfrac{175}{100} = \dfrac{7}{4}$ (note that fractions larger than 1, such as this, are often referred to as *improper* or *vulgar fractions*)

Exercises

1.   What is the value of the 7 in each of these numbers:

(a)	0.714	(b)	0.070	(c)	7.042
(d)	0.007	(e)	0.471	(f)	0.157

2.   Write each list of numbers in order with the smallest first:

     (a)   0.61, 0.16, 0.601, 0.106, 0.661, 0.616

     (b)   0.47, 0.82, 0.4, 0.78, 0.28

     (c)   0.32, 0.23, 0.2, 0.301, 0.3

     (d)   0.17, 0.19, 0.9, 0.91, 0.79

3.	Write each of these decimals as a fraction, giving them in their simplest form:

(a)	0.1

(b)	0.9

(c)	0.3

(d)	0.07

(e)	0.25

(f)	0.001

(g)	0.05

(h)	0.003

(i)	0.017

(j)	0.71

(k)	0.87

(l)	0.201

4.	Write each of these decimals as a fraction and simplify where possible:

(a)	0.4

(b)	0.08

(c)	0.54

(d)	0.006

(e)	0.012

(f)	0.162

(g)	0.048

(h)	0.84

(i)	0.328

(j)	0.014

(k)	0.006

(l)	0.108

5.	Write down the missing numbers:

(a)	$0.6 = \dfrac{?}{5}$

(b)	$0.14 = \dfrac{?}{50}$

(c)	$0.18 = \dfrac{?}{50}$

(d)	$0.008 = \dfrac{?}{125}$

(e)	$0.012 = \dfrac{?}{250}$

(f)	$0.016 = \dfrac{?}{125}$

6.	Write these numbers as *improper fractions* in their simplest form:

(a)	1.2

(b)	3.02

(c)	4.12

(d)	3.62

(e)	4.008

(f)	5.015

7.	Calculate, giving your answers as decimals *and* as fractions:

(a)	$0.7 + 0.6$

(b)	$0.8 - 0.3$

(c)	$0.71 + 0.62$

(d)	$8.21 - 0.31$

(e)	$0.06 + 0.3$

(f)	$1.7 + 0.21$

(g)	$8.06 - 0.2$

(h)	$0.42 - 0.002$

8.	Write the missing numbers as decimals and convert them to fractions in their simplest form:

(a)	$0.20 + \; ? \; = 0.81$

(b)	$0.42 + \; ? \; = 0.53$

(c)	$0.91 - \; ? \; = 0.47$

(d)	$0.92 - \; ? \; = 0.58$

9.   Convert these decimals to fractions:

(a)   0.0001   (b)   0.0009

(c)   0.00021   (d)   0.123491

10.   Convert these decimals to fractions in their simplest form:

(a)   0.00008   (b)   0.02222

(c)   0.00102   (d)   0.000004

(e)   0.000224   (f)   0.0000002

17.2 Conversion: Fractions into Decimals

In this section we consider how to write fractions as decimals.

Example 1

Write these fractions as decimals:

(a) $\dfrac{7}{10}$ (b) $\dfrac{81}{100}$ (c) $\dfrac{9}{1000}$ (d) $\dfrac{407}{1000}$

Solution

(a) $\dfrac{7}{10} = 0.7$

(b) $\dfrac{81}{100} = 0.81$

(c) $\dfrac{9}{1000} = 0.009$

(d) $\dfrac{407}{1000} = 0.407$

Example 2

Write these fractions as decimals:

(a) $\dfrac{2}{5}$ (b) $\dfrac{3}{50}$ (c) $\dfrac{6}{25}$ (d) $\dfrac{5}{4}$ (e) $\dfrac{7}{250}$

Solution

In each case, determine the equivalent fraction with the denominator as either 10, 100 or 1000. The fractions can then be written as decimals.

(a) $\dfrac{2}{5} = \dfrac{4}{10} = 0.4$

(b) $\dfrac{3}{50} = \dfrac{6}{100} = 0.06$

(c) $\dfrac{6}{25} = \dfrac{24}{100} = 0.24$

(d) $\dfrac{5}{4} = \dfrac{125}{100} = 1.25$

(e) $\dfrac{7}{250} = \dfrac{28}{1000} = 0.028$

Example 3

(a) Calculate $18 \div 5$, then write $\dfrac{18}{5}$ as a decimal.

(b) Calculate $5 \div 8$, then write $\dfrac{5}{8}$ as a decimal.

Solution

(a) $18 \div 5 = 3.6$, since

$$5 \overline{)18.^30}$$
$$3.6$$

So $\dfrac{18}{5} = 18 \div 5$

$= 3.6$

(b) $5 \div 8 = 0.625$, since

$$8 \overline{)5.0^20^40}$$
$$0.625$$

So $\dfrac{5}{8} = 5 \div 8$

$= 0.625$

Exercises

1. Write these fractions as decimals:

(a) $\dfrac{3}{10}$

(b) $\dfrac{7}{100}$

(c) $\dfrac{9}{1000}$

(d) $\dfrac{13}{100}$

(e) $\dfrac{131}{1000}$

(f) $\dfrac{47}{1000}$

(g) $\dfrac{21}{100}$

(h) $\dfrac{183}{1000}$

(i) $\dfrac{19}{100}$

(j) $\dfrac{19}{1000}$

(k) $\dfrac{11}{100}$

(l) $\dfrac{81}{1000}$

2. Calculate the missing numbers:

(a) $\dfrac{?}{2} = \dfrac{5}{10}$

(b) $\dfrac{?}{20} = \dfrac{35}{100}$

(c) $\dfrac{?}{25} = \dfrac{8}{100}$

(d) $\dfrac{?}{4} = \dfrac{25}{100}$

(e) $\dfrac{2}{?} = \dfrac{4}{100}$

(f) $\dfrac{6}{?} = \dfrac{12}{1000}$

(g) $\dfrac{8}{?} = \dfrac{32}{100}$

(h) $\dfrac{7}{?} = \dfrac{28}{100}$

3. Write these fractions as decimals:

(a) $\dfrac{1}{2}$

(b) $\dfrac{4}{5}$

(c) $\dfrac{9}{50}$

(d) $\dfrac{3}{25}$

(e) $\dfrac{3}{20}$

(f) $\dfrac{3}{500}$

(g) $\dfrac{1}{250}$

(h) $\dfrac{7}{20}$

(i) $\dfrac{61}{200}$

(j) $\dfrac{18}{25}$

(k) $\dfrac{9}{125}$

(l) $\dfrac{1}{4}$

4. Write these improper fractions as decimals:

(a) $\dfrac{12}{10}$

(b) $\dfrac{212}{100}$

(c) $\dfrac{5218}{1000}$

(d) $\dfrac{2008}{100}$ (e) $\dfrac{2008}{1000}$ (f) $\dfrac{418}{10}$

5. Write these improper fractions as decimals:

   (a) $\dfrac{7}{2}$ (b) $\dfrac{21}{20}$ (c) $\dfrac{33}{20}$

   (d) $\dfrac{31}{25}$ (e) $\dfrac{16}{5}$ (f) $\dfrac{1001}{500}$

6. Write as a fraction and as a decimal:

   (a) $3 \div 5$ (b) $3 \div 8$ (c) $25 \div 4$

   (d) $16 \div 5$ (e) $26 \div 4$ (f) $30 \div 8$

7. (a) Calculate $7 \div 8$.

   (b) Write $\dfrac{7}{8}$ as a decimal.

8. (a) Calculate $41 \div 5$.

   (b) Write $\dfrac{41}{5}$ as a decimal.

9. Write $\dfrac{1}{8}$ as a decimal by using division.

10. Write $\dfrac{13}{16}$ as a decimal.

17.3 Introduction to Percentages

The word 'percentage' means 'per hundred'. In this section we look at how percentages can be used as an alternative to fractions or decimals.

$$100\% = \frac{100}{100} = 1$$

$$50\% = \frac{50}{100} = \frac{1}{2}$$

$$1\% = \frac{1}{100}$$

Example 1

Draw diagrams to show:

(a)   71%

(b)   20%

(c)   5%

Solution

These percentages can be shown by shading a suitable fraction of a 10 by 10 square shape.

(a) $71\% = \dfrac{71}{100}$,   so $\dfrac{71}{100}$ of a shape needs to be shaded:

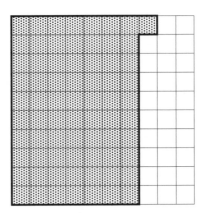

(b) $20\% = \dfrac{20}{100} = \dfrac{1}{5}$,   so $\dfrac{1}{5}$ of a shape needs to be shaded:

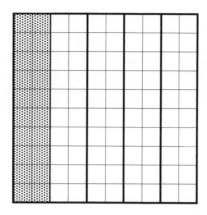

(c) $5\% = \dfrac{5}{100} = \dfrac{1}{20}$, so $\dfrac{1}{20}$ of a shape needs to be shaded:

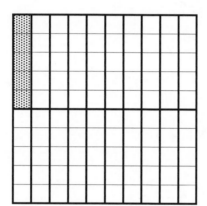

Example 2

(a)   What percentage of this shape is shaded?

(b)   What percentage of this shape is *not* shaded?

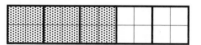

Solution

(a) $\dfrac{3}{5}$ of the shape is shaded, and

$$\frac{3}{5} = \frac{6}{10}$$

$$= \frac{60}{100},$$

so 60% is shaded.

(b) $100 - 60 = 40$, so 40% is *not* shaded.

17.3

Example 3

Find:

(a)   5% of 100 kg,

(b)   20% of 40 m,

(c)   25% of £80.

Solution

(a)   5% of 100 kg $= \dfrac{5}{100} \times 100$

$= \dfrac{1}{20} \times 100$

$= 5 \text{ kg}$

(b)   20% of 40 m $= \dfrac{20}{100} \times 40$

$= \dfrac{1}{5} \times 40$

$= 8 \text{ m}$

(c)   25% of £80 $= \dfrac{25}{100} \times 80$

$= \dfrac{1}{4} \times 80$

$= £20$

Exercises

1.   For each diagram, state the percentage that is shaded:

(a)

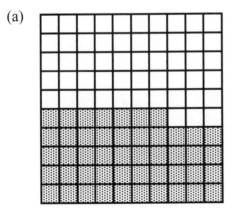

(b)

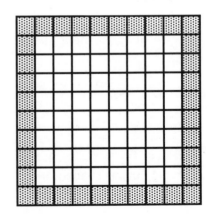

(c) 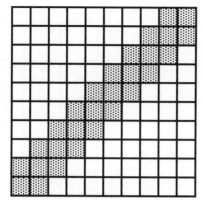 (d)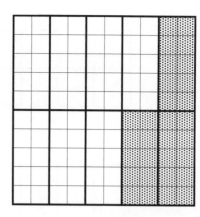

(e) 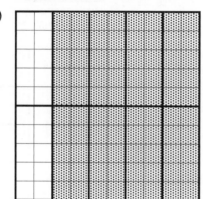 (f)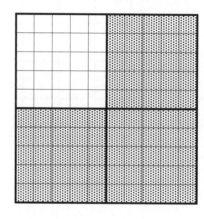

2.   For each diagram in question 1, state the percentage that is *not* shaded.

3.   If 76% of a rectangle is shaded, what percentage is *not* shaded?

4.   Make 4 copies of this diagram
     and shade the percentage stated:

     (a)   23%

     (b)   50%

     (c)   79%

     (d)   87%

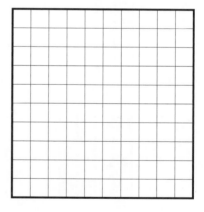

5.   Copy each diagram and shade the percentage stated:

     (a)   25%

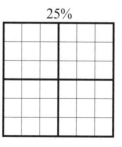

           (b)   30%

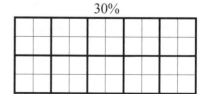

17.3

(c)   90%

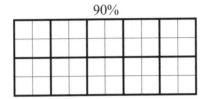

(d)   5%

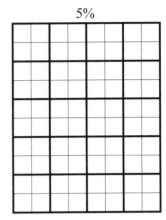

(e)   15%

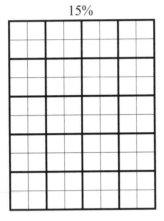

(f)   65%

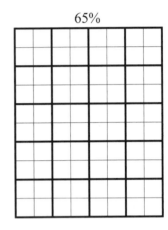

6.   State the shaded percentage of each shape:

(a)   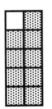   (b)   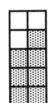   (c)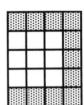

(d)   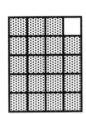   (e)   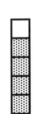   (f)   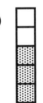   (g)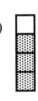

7.   If 35% of a class are girls, what percentage are boys?

8.   If 88% of a class pass a maths test, what percentage fail the test?

9.   Calculate:

(a)   50% of £200,   (b)   30% of 500 kg,

(c)   60% of 50p,   (d)   5% of £2,

(e)   15% of 10 kg,   (f)   25% of 120 m,

(g)   2% of £400,   (h)   26% of £2,

(i)   20% of £300,   (j)   75% of 200 kg.

10.   Ben and Adam spend their Saturdays cleaning cars. They agree that Adam will have 60% of the money they earn and that Ben will have the rest.

(a)   What percentage of the money will Ben have?

(b)   How much do they each have if they earn £25?

(c)   How much do they each have if they earn £30?

17.4 Decimals, Fractions and Percentages

In this section we concentrate in converting between decimals, fractions and percentages.

Example 1

Write these percentages as decimals:

(a)   72%   (b)   3%

Solution

(a) $72\% = \dfrac{72}{100}$

$= 0.72$

(b) $3\% = \dfrac{3}{100}$

$= 0.03$

Example 2

Write these decimals as percentages:

(a)   0.71   (b)   0.4   (c)   0.06

Solution

(a) $0.71 = \dfrac{71}{100}$

$= 71\%$

(b) 0.4 $= \dfrac{4}{10}$

$ = \dfrac{40}{100}$

$ = 40\%$

(c) 0.06 $= \dfrac{6}{100}$

$ = 6\%$

Example 3

Write these percentages as fractions in their simplest possible form:

(a) 90% (b) 20% (c) 5%

Solution

(a) 90% $= \dfrac{90}{100}$

$ = \dfrac{9}{10}$

(b) 20% $= \dfrac{20}{100}$

$ = \dfrac{1}{5}$

(c) 5% $= \dfrac{5}{100}$

$ = \dfrac{1}{20}$

Example 4

Write these fractions as percentages:

(a) $\dfrac{1}{2}$ (b) $\dfrac{2}{5}$ (c) $\dfrac{7}{20}$

Solution

(a) $\dfrac{1}{2}$ $= \dfrac{50}{100}$

$\phantom{(a)\ \dfrac{1}{2}\ } = 50\%$

(b) $\dfrac{2}{5} = \dfrac{40}{100}$

  $= 40\%$

(c) $\dfrac{7}{20} = \dfrac{35}{100}$

  $= 35\%$

Exercises

1. Write these percentages as decimals:

   (a) 42%   (b) 37%   (c) 20%

   (d) 5%   (e) 8%   (f) 10%

   (g) 22%   (h) 3%   (i) 15%

2. Write these decimals as percentages:

   (a) 0.14   (b) 0.72   (c) 0.55

   (d) 0.4   (e) 0.03   (f) 0.9

   (g) 0.18   (h) 0.04   (i) 0.7

3. Write these percentages as fractions in their simplest forms:

   (a) 50%   (b) 30%   (c) 80%

   (d) 70%   (e) 15%   (f) 25%

   (g) 64%   (h) 98%   (i) 56%

4. Write these fractions as percentages:

   (a) $\dfrac{7}{100}$ (b) $\dfrac{18}{100}$ (c) $\dfrac{3}{50}$

   (d) $\dfrac{17}{50}$ (e) $\dfrac{3}{20}$ (f) $\dfrac{7}{25}$

   (g) $\dfrac{3}{5}$ (h) $\dfrac{7}{10}$ (i) $\dfrac{3}{4}$

   (j) $\dfrac{1}{20}$ (k) $\dfrac{1}{2}$ (l) $\dfrac{3}{25}$

5. Copy and complete this table:

Fraction	Decimal	Percentage
	0.04	
		10%
$\frac{1}{2}$		
		45%
$\frac{7}{50}$		
	0.84	

6. There are 200 children in a school hall, eating lunch. Of these children, 124 have chosen chips as part of their lunch.

    (a)   What *fraction* of the children have chosen chips?

    (b)   What *percentage* of the children have chosen chips?

    (c)   What percentage of the children have *not* chosen chips?

7. In a survey, $\frac{9}{10}$ of the children in a school said that maths was their favourite subject. What percentage of the children *did not* say that maths was their favourite subject?

8. In a Year 7 class, $\frac{3}{4}$ of the children can swim more than 400 m and only $\frac{1}{10}$ of the children can not swim more than 200 m.

    What percentage of the class can swim:

    (a)   more than 400 m,

    (b)   less than 200 m,

    (c)   a distance between 200 m and 400 m?

9. In the school canteen, children can choose chips, baked potato or rice. One day 50% choose chips and 26% choose baked potatoes.

    (a)   What percentage choose rice?

    (b)   What fraction of the children choose rice?

10. In a car park, 40% of the cars are red and $\frac{7}{20}$ of the cars are blue.

    (a)   What *percentage* are blue?

    (b)   What *percentage* are *neither* red *nor* blue?

    (c)   What *percentage* are red or blue?

    (d)   What *fraction* are red?

    (e)   What *fraction* are *neither* red *nor* blue?

    (f)   What *fraction* are red or blue?

18 Quantitative Data

18.1 Presentation

In this section we look at how vertical line diagrams can be used to display discrete quantitative data. (Remember that discrete data can only take specific numerical values.)

Example 1

The marks below were scored by the children in a class on their maths test. The marks are all out of a possible total of 10 marks.

$$
\begin{array}{ccccc}
8 & 6 & 8 & 7 & 7 \\
7 & 10 & 9 & 6 & 8 \\
8 & 4 & 3 & 2 & 5 \\
8 & 8 & 6 & 5 & 6 \\
4 & 9 & 8 & 4 & 7 \\
7 & 5 & 3 & 7 & 6 \\
\end{array}
$$

Draw a vertical line diagram to illustrate these data.

Use your diagram to answer these questions:

(a) What is the *most common* mark?

(b) What is the *highest* mark?

(c) What is the *lowest* mark?

(d) What is the difference between the *highest* and *lowest* marks?

Solution

The first step is to organise the data using a *tally chart*, as shown here:

Mark	Tally	Frequency
2	|	1
3	||	2
4	|||	3
5	|||	3
6	⪫⪫⪫	5
7	⪫⪫⪫ |	6
8	⪫⪫⪫ ||	7
9	||	2
10	|	1

The diagram can then be drawn as shown below. The height of each line is the same as the frequency; that is, the number of times it occurs in the data list.

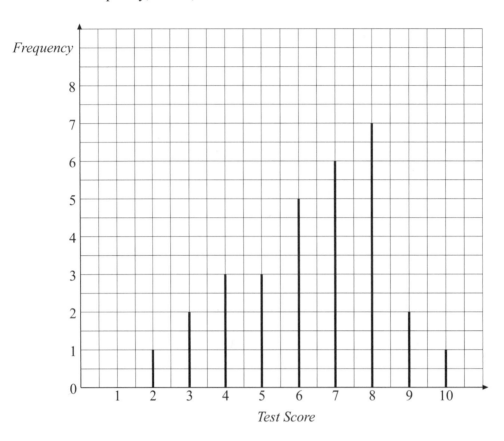

(a) The *most common* mark is 8, which occurred 7 times.

(b) The *highest* mark is 10.

(c) The *lowest* mark is 2.

(d) The difference between the *highest* and *lowest* marks is $10 - 2 = 8$.

Note: a *vertical line diagram* is an appropriate way to represent information that consists of distinct, single values, each with its own frequency. A *bar graph* is more suitable for grouped numerical data.

Exercises

1. A teacher gives the children in her class a test, and lists their scores in this table:

   (a) Draw a vertical line diagram to illustrate these results.

   (b) What is the *most common* mark?

   (c) How many children are there in the class?

Mark	Frequency
1	1
2	4
3	1
4	3
5	6
6	8
7	4
8	2

2. The staff in a shoe shop keep a record of the sizes of all the shoes they sell in one day. These are listed below:

     8   7   6   6   8   7   5   4   3   1
    11   7   8   9   5   6   6   5   6   4
     3   10   8   9   7   6   6   5   4   2
     6   9   11   3   5   6   7   8   8   3
     4   6   7   8   9   8   8   7   6   4

    (a) Complete a tally chart for these data.

    (b) Draw a vertical line diagram for these data.

    (c) What advice could you give the shop staff about which size shoes they should keep in stock?

3. The vertical line diagram below is based on data collected by a class about the number of children in their families:

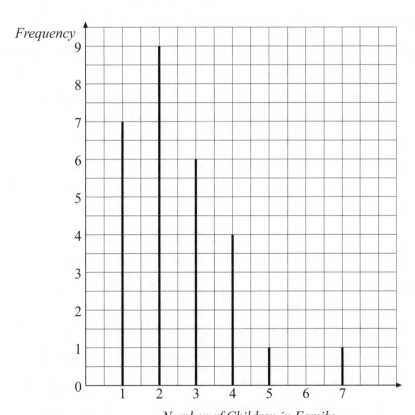

    Number of Children in Family

    (a) What is the *most common* number of children per family?

    (b) How many children are there in the class?

4.   (a)   Collect data on the number of children in the families of the pupils in
             your mathematics class.

      (b)   Draw a vertical line diagram like the one in question 3.

      (c)   Compare your vertical line diagram with the one for question 3.
             What *similarities* are there? What *differences* are there?

5.   Mr Graddon says that his class is better at tables than Mr Hall's class. The
      two classes each take a tables test, and the results are given below. The
      scores are out of 10.

Mr Graddon's Class						*Mr Hall's Class*					
5	6	7	8	9	10	4	7	8	3	5	6
0	1	3	6	9	2	7	4	5	6	6	5
5	1	2	2	0	1	5	5	6	7	4	3
6	4	0	1	10	9	4	5	6	6	7	8
1	2	3	5	10	9	6	7	5	6	4	5

      (a)   Draw a vertical line diagram for each class.

      (b)   Which features of the two diagrams would Mr Graddon use to support
             his claim that his class is better at tables?

      (c)   How would Mr Hall use the diagrams to argue the other way?

      (d)   Which class do *you* think is better at tables?

6.   A gardener keeps a record of the number of tomatoes he picks from the
      plants in his greenhouse during August. The number of tomatoes picked
      each day is listed below:

7	10	3	6	8	9	5	10	4	7	9
6	10	11	12	13	7	8	4	3	6	9
7	9	10	11	14	13	7	8	9		

      (a)   Draw a vertical line diagram for these data.

      (b)   What is the *largest* number of tomatoes picked on one day?

      (c)   What is the *smallest* number of tomatoes picked on one day?

      (d)   What is the number of tomatoes that was picked *most often*?

7.   A sample of children were asked how many pets they had, and their
      responses are listed below:

4	1	1	0	2	0	1	3	4	0
1	0	1	2	0	1	1	3	0	5

(a) Draw a vertical line diagram for these data.

(b) How many pets were in the sample?

(c) How many children owned at least one pet?

(d) Is it true that, in this sample, there are more children who own pets than children who do not?

8. A rail company keeps a record of how many trains are late each day. The data for January are listed below:

2	0	3	0	1	1	2	0	3	0	4
6	1	0	0	0	2	1	3	1	0	
0	0	1	2	3	1	1	1	2	3	

The data for February are listed below:

3	2	4	7	0	1	2	0	1	2
0	0	0	1	0	1	2	1	2	0
0	2	1	3	1	2	1	1		

(a) Draw vertical line diagrams for each month.

(b) Comment on whether the trains were on time more often in February than in January.

9. A traffic warden keeps a record of the number of parking tickets that she issues on 20 working days.

0	3	7	8	12	0	1	3	4	5
6	5	4	0	1	3	4	6	7	5

(a) Draw a vertical line diagram for these data.

(b) How many blank parking tickets do you think she should take with her when she starts her daily traffic patrol? Explain your answer.

10. Graham uses his calculator to generate random numbers. He decides to investigate if the numbers are really random. Using his calculator, he produces the following numbers:

9	9	1	5	4	7	0	3	9	2
7	9	2	3	0	9	1	0	5	8
9	2	2	1	0	7	0	4	3	9
0	8	6	2	9	7	3	2	9	9

(a)   Draw a vertical line diagram for these data.

(b)   Do you think that the numbers that Graham's calculator produces are really random? Explain your answer.

18.2   Measures of Central Tendency

In this section we will consider three different types of 'average'. These are the *mean,* the *median* and the *mode*, and statisticians refer to them as *measures of central tendency.*

$$Mean = \frac{sum\ of\ all\ values}{total\ number\ of\ values}$$

$$Median = middle\ value\ (when\ the\ data\ are\ arranged\ in\ order)$$

$$Mode = most\ common\ value$$

Measures of central tendency are single values chosen as being representative of a whole data set. When we select which of the mean, the median or the mode to use, we choose the one that we think is most typical of the data and appropriate for the context.

Example 1

What is:

(a)   the *mean,*   (b)   the *median* and   (c)   the *mode*

of the numbers:

$$4, \ 7, \ 8, \ 4, \ 5$$

Solution

(a)   *Mean* $= \dfrac{4 + 7 + 8 + 4 + 5}{5}$

$= \dfrac{28}{5}$

$= 5.6$

(b)   To calculate the *median*, write the numbers in order,

$$4, \ 4, \ \boxed{5,} \ 7, \ 8$$

The middle number is 5,

median = 5

(c)   The most common number is 4, so

mode   = 4

Example 2

What number is the *median* of the numbers:

$$4, \ 7, \ 11, \ 4, \ 6, \ 7, \ 2, \ 9$$

Solution

First write the numbers in order:

$$2, \ 4, \ 4, \ \boxed{6, \ 7,} \ 7, \ 9, \ 11$$

In this case there are two middle numbers, 6 and 7. The *median* is the mean of these two numbers:

$$Median \ = \ \frac{6 + 7}{2}$$

$$= \ 6.5$$

Note: where there is an *odd* number of data items, there will be a single value in the middle and that will be the median – provided you have arranged the data in order. When there is an *even* number of data items, there will be two values in the middle and you must find their mean to get the median of the full data set.

Example 3

David keeps a record of the number of carrier bags that he is given when he does his weekly shopping. The data he collects over 10 weeks is listed below:

$$9 \qquad 8 \qquad 5 \qquad 9 \qquad 12 \qquad 8 \qquad 7 \qquad 6 \qquad 5 \qquad 9$$

(a)   Calculate: (i)   the *mean*, (ii) the *median*,   (iii) the *mode*?

(b)   Explain why the mean is not very useful in this context.

(c)   Which value might be used by an environmental group who think that supermarkets cause pollution by giving out too many carrier bags?

(d)   Which value might be used by a shopper who thinks that the supermarket doesn't give him enough carrier bags for his shopping?

Solution

(a)   (i) $Mean \ = \ \dfrac{9 + 8 + 5 + 9 + 12 + 8 + 7 + 6 + 5 + 9}{10}$

$$= \frac{78}{10}$$

$$= 7.8$$

(ii)   To find the *median*, put the numbers in order, and find the middle numbers:

5   5   6   7   8   8   9   9   9   12

$$Median \ = \ \frac{8 + 8}{2}$$

$$= 8$$

(iii)   The most common number is 9:

Mode = 9

(b)   The mean is not very useful as no one would ever actually use 7.8 plastic bags.

(c)   The mode, as this is the largest of the three values.

(d)   The mean, as this is the smallest of the three values.

Exercises

1.   Find the *mean, median* and *mode* of each set of numbers:

(a)   4   4   6   8   5

(b)   6   7   7   7   7   5   6   2   9   8

(c)   8   4   3   3   5   7

(d)   6   6   7   7   4   9   1   7   10

2.   The owner of a shoe shop recorded the sizes of the feet of all the customers who bought shoes in his shop in one morning. These sizes are listed below:

8   7   4   5   9   13   10   8   8   7

6   5   3   11   10   8   5   4   8   6

(a)   What are the *mean, median* and *mode* shoe sizes?

(b)   Which of these values would be most sensible for the shop owner to use when ordering shoes for his shop? Explain your choice.

3.   Eight people work in a shop. They are paid hourly rates of

£4   £15   £6   £5   £4   £5   £4   £4

Would you use the *mean, median* or *mode* to show that they were:

(a)   *well* paid,   (b)   *badly* paid?

4. A newspaper reports that the average number of children per family is 2.4.

   (a) Which type of value has the newspaper used?

   (b) Explain how you can tell which value was used.

   (c) Would your answer to (b) be the same if the newspaper had reported the average as 2.5 children?

5. The mean of six numbers is 9. If five of the numbers are 10, 12, 7, 6 and 9, what is the sixth number?

6. The table below gives the number of accidents each year at a particular road junction:

1991	1992	1993	1994	1995	1996	1997	1998
4	5	4	2	10	5	3	5

   (a) Calculate the *mean, median* and *mode*.

   (b) Describe which value would be most sensible for a road safety group to use, if they want the junction to be made less dangerous.

   (c) The council do not want to spend money on the road junction. Which value do you think they should use?

7. One day the number of minutes that trains were late to arrive at a station was recorded. The times are listed below:

0	7	0	0	1	2	5	0	0	0
6	0	1	52	0	10	1	1	8	22

   (a) Calculate the *mean, median* and *mode* of these data.

   (b) Explain which value would be the best to use to argue that the trains arrive late too often.

   (c) Explain who might use the mode and why it might be an advantage to them.

8. Mr Hall grows two different types of tomato plant in his greenhouse. One week he keeps a record of the number of tomatoes he picks from each type of plant.

Day	Mon	Tues	Wed	Thurs	Fri	Sat	Sun
Type A	5	5	4	1	0	2	5
Type B	3	3	3	3	7	9	6

(a)   Calculate the *mean, median* and *mode* for each type of plant.

(b)   Use one value to argue that type A is the best plant.

(c)   Use a different value to argue that type B is the best plant.

9.   The heights of eight children are given below, to the nearest cm:

       158   162   142   155   163   157   160   112

(a)   Explain why the mode is *not* a suitable value to use for these data.

(b)   Calculate the median and the mean of these data.

(c)   Explain why the mean is less than the median.

10.   A set contains four positive numbers.

The *mode* of these numbers is 1.

The *mean* of these numbers is 2.5.

The *median* of these numbers is 1.5.

What are the four numbers?

18.3   Measures of Dispersion

The *range* of a set of data is the difference between the largest and the smallest values in the data set. The range gives a measure of the dispersion of the data, or, more simply, describes the spread of the data.

Example 1

Calculate the *range* of this set of data:

       4   7   6   8   3   9   14   22   3

Solution

The largest value is 22.

The smallest value is 3.

$Range = 22 - 3$

$= 19$

Example 2

What is the *range* of the data illustrated in this vertical line diagram?

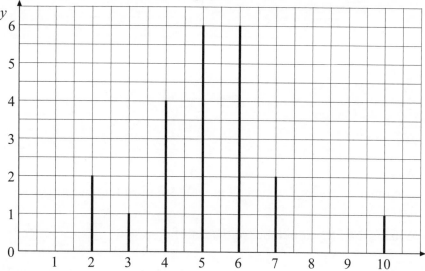

Solution

Largest value = 10

Smallest value = 2

Range   = 10 − 2

                = 8

Exercises

1. Calculate the *range* of each of these sets of data:

    (a)   4   7   6   3   9   12   7   12

    (b)   6   5   5   16   12   21   42   7

    (c)   0   2   4   1   3   0   6

    (d)   3   7   8   9   4   7   11

18.3

2. Calculate the *range* of the data illustrated in this vertical line diagram:

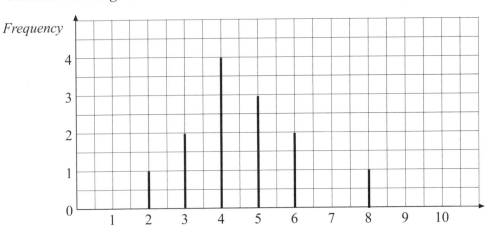

3. The range of a set of data is 12 and the smallest number in the set of data is 5.

What is the *largest* number in the set of data?

4. The largest number in a set of data is 86. The range of the set of data is 47. What is the *smallest* number in the set of data?

5. The heights of 10 students were measured to the nearest centimetre and are listed below:

$$144 \quad 162 \quad 173 \quad 158 \quad 143$$
$$159 \quad 164 \quad 182 \quad 162 \quad 158$$

What is the *range* of this set of data?

6. Rafiq keeps a record of the amount of money he spends each day. The amounts for one week are listed below:

$$47p \quad 10p \quad 36p \quad 85p \quad 22p \quad 30p$$

There are only 6 amounts because he forgets to include one day.

(a) What is the *range* of the numbers listed above?

(b) If the range was 90p, what was the missing amount?

(c) If the range was double your answer to (a), what was the missing amount?

(d) Explain why the range must be equal to or greater than your answer to part (a).

7. The vertical line diagram on the following page is for a data set that has one missing value.

What can you say about the missing value if the range is:

(a) 7, (b) 9, (c) 6 ?

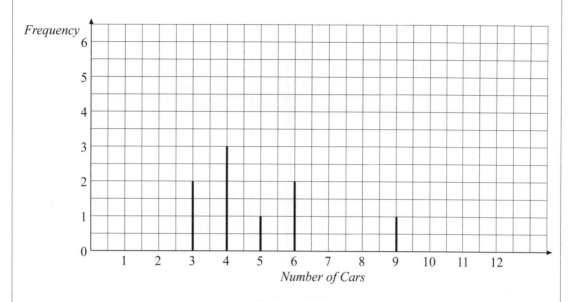

8. What is the range of this set of temperatures:

$-4\,°C$ $3\,°C$ $5\,°C$ $-1\,°C$ $-3\,°C$ $6\,°C$?

9. The range of a set of temperatures is $8\,°C$. If the *maximum* temperature in the set is $6\,°C$, what is the *minimum* temperature?

10. The range of a set of temperatures is $7\,°C$. If the *minimum* temperature in the set is $-11\,°C$ what is the *maximum* temperature?

18.4 Comparing Data

In this section we consider how averages and the range can be used to compare sets of data.

Example 1

The two line diagrams on the next page illustrate data that was collected about the scores of two groups of children in a short test.

(a) Calculate the *mode* and *range* for each group.

(b) Describe the differences between the groups.

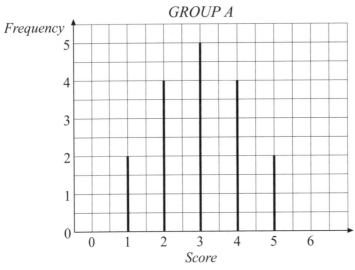

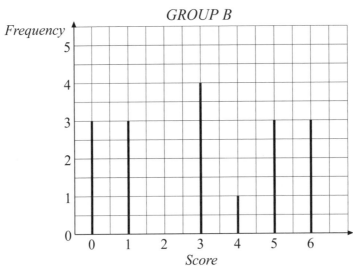

Solution

(a)

Group A		Group B	
Mode	= 3	*Mode*	= 3
Range	= 5 − 1		= 6 − 0
	= 4		= 6

(b) Both groups have the same mode but different ranges. The range is greater for group B.

The low range for group A indicates that the scores for those students are reasonably similar. The higher range for group B shows that their scores are much more varied. This can be seen from the line diagrams, where none of group A get the extreme scores of 0 and 6, while these are obtained by several students in group B.

Example 2

Kathryn plants two different types of tomato plant. She records the number of tomatoes that she picks from each plant every day for 10 days. Her records are shown below:

Plant A	4	6	7	3	5	2	1	3	6	5
Plant B	5	6	7	6	8	9	6	7	8	9

Compare the two plants and recommend which type she should buy next year.

Solution

First consider the mean and range for each plant:

$$PLANT\ A$$

$$Mean = \frac{4 + 6 + 7 + 3 + 5 + 2 + 1 + 3 + 6 + 5}{10}$$

$$= \frac{42}{10}$$

$$= 4.2$$

$$Range = 7 - 1$$

$$= 6$$

$$PLANT\ B$$

$$Mean = \frac{5 + 6 + 7 + 6 + 8 + 9 + 6 + 7 + 8 + 9}{10}$$

$$= \frac{71}{10}$$

$$= 7.1$$

$$Range = 9 - 5$$

$$= 4$$

As plant B has a higher mean, this suggests that using plant B will produce more tomatoes than using plants of type A. The fact the plant B has the lower range suggests that it will also be more consistent in the number of tomatoes that it produces than type A. Type A will have some productive days but it will also have some poor days.

18.4

Exercises

1. (a) Calculate the *mean* and *range* of these two data sets:

A	5	10	0	1	9	5
B	5	6	4	3	7	5

    (b) Describe the difference between the two sets.

2. (a) Calculate the *mean* and *range* of these two data sets:

A	4	6	7	8	5	6.
B	5	7	7	8	9	6

    (b) Describe the difference between the two sets.

3. (a) Calculate the *mean* and *range* of these two data sets:

A	4	6	10	3	5	2
B	6	7	9	9	5	3

    (b) Describe the differences between the two sets.

4. (a) Calculate the *mean* and *range* of these 3 sets of data:

A	4	7	8	6	5	
B	0	10	12	1	3	
C	8	8	9	10	9	8

    (b) Describe the differences between the three sets.

5. Roy and Frank are second-hand car salesmen. The following vertical line diagrams show how many cars they have sold per week over a period of time.

    (a) Write down the *mode* for Roy and for Frank.

    (b) Calculate the *range* for Roy and for Frank.

    (c) Who sold more cars?

    (d) Who you think is the better salesman? Explain why.

ROY

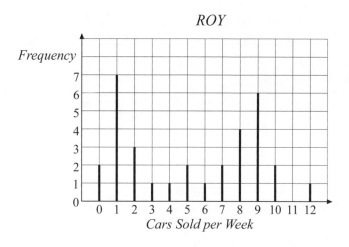

FRANK

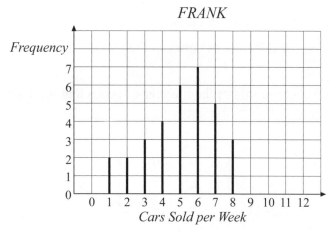

6. The two vertical line diagrams show the number of goals scored per match by two top footballers.

ANDY GOAL

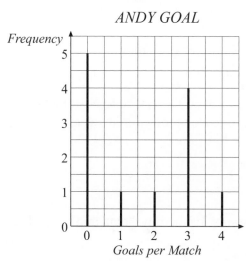

ALAN SCORER

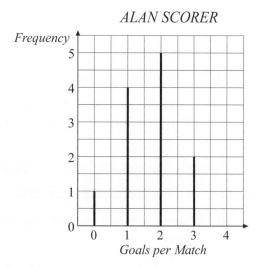

(a) Calculate the *mean* and *range* for each player.

(b) Describe the differences between the two players.

(c) Which of these players would you like to have on your favourite team? Explain why.

7. Miss Sharp's class decide to have a spelling competition with Mr Berry's class. They have a test and the scores for each class are listed below:

Miss Sharp's Class							*Mr Berry's Class*					
10	1	5	8	5	7		5	5	7	6	7	8
2	6	8	7	5	9		5	4	3	3	2	5
2	4	8	0	5	3		4	5	6	5	4	6
5	10	2	5	7	1		7	7	6	4	3	5
5	5	3	3	0	9		3	5	5	6	4	5

    (a)   Calculate the *mean* for each class.

    (b)   Calculate the *range* for each class.

    (c)   Comment on the differences between the two classes.

8. A bus company keeps records of the number of buses that were late each day in February and in July in the same year:

February

6	7	5	4	3	0	0	1	2	5	
9	10	5	4	3	6	7	1	0	0	
0	0	1	2	1	0	4	1			

July

3	0	1	0	3	1	2	3	4	9	1
2	0	4	1	1	2	3	4	1	5	
7	2	1	2	3	0	4	1	0	2	

    (a)   Calculate the *mean, median* and *mode* for each month.

    (b)   Calculate the *range* for each month.

    (c)   Do you think the bus company improved its service to customers between February and July? Give reasons for your answer.

9. "Do boys have bigger feet than girls?"

    (a)   Collect data from your class.

    (b)   Draw separate vertical line diagrams for the boys' data and the girls' data.

    (c)   Calculate the *mode, mean, median* and *range* for each set of data.

    (d)   Use your diagrams and calculations to decide, for your class, the answer to the question above.

10. Investigate whether girls eat more fruit than boys.

18.5 | Trends

Moving averages can be used to make predictions. They do this by smoothing out monthly, seasonal or other periodic variations.

For example, an ice-cream seller might expect to sell more in the summer than he does in the winter. He could use a moving average over the four seasons to find out if his sales are increasing for each 12 month period.

$$\textit{1st moving average} \quad = \quad \frac{\text{spring 1} + \text{summer 1} + \text{autumn 1} + \text{winter 1}}{4}$$

$$\textit{2nd moving average} \quad = \quad \frac{\text{summer 1} + \text{autumn 1} + \text{winter 1} + \text{spring 2}}{4}$$

$$\textit{3rd moving average} \quad = \quad \frac{\text{autumn 1} + \text{winter 1} + \text{spring 2} + \text{summer 2}}{4}$$

$$\textit{4th moving average} \quad = \quad \frac{\text{winter 1} + \text{spring 2} + \text{summer 2} + \text{autumn 2}}{4}$$

and so on. In each case, the oldest piece of data is replaced by the newest one. So, for the *fifth moving average*, the ice-cream seller would replace the winter sales figure for the first year with the winter sales figure for the second year, and so on. Because the mean of four items of data is being found every time, this is called a *4 point* moving average.

Example 1

(a) Calculate the 4 point moving averages for this list of data:

$$6 \quad 5 \quad 7 \quad 4 \quad 6.1 \quad 5.1 \quad 7.1 \quad 4.1$$

(b) Estimate the next two values in the list.

Solution

(a)   *1st moving average* $= \dfrac{6 + 5 + 7 + 4}{4}$

                     $= 5.5$

     2nd moving average $= \dfrac{5 + 7 + 4 + 6.1}{4}$

                     $= 5.525$

     3rd moving average $= \dfrac{7 + 4 + 6.1 + 5.1}{4}$

                     $= 5.55$

     4th moving average $= \dfrac{4 + 6.1 + 5.1 + 7.1}{4}$

                     $= 5.575$

$$5th\ moving\ average\ =\ \frac{6.1 + 5.1 + 7.1 + 4.1}{4}$$

$$=\ 5.6$$

(b)   Note that the moving averages increase by 0.025 at each step.

The next moving average will be expected to be 5.625, so

$$5.625 \times 4\ =\ 5.1 + 7.1 + 4.1 + x$$

where x is the next term.

$$x\ =\ 5.625 \times 4 - 5.1 - 7.1 - 4.1$$

$$=\ 6.2$$

To estimate the next value, we use

$$5.65 \times 4 - 7.1 - 4.1 - 6.2\ =\ 5.2$$

Example 2

The table below gives the average daytime temperatures for each of the four seasons over a two-year period.

Year 1				Year 2			
Spring	Summer	Autumn	Winter	Spring	Summer	Autumn	Winter
12.1	18.6	11.2	8.1	12.4	19.0	11.8	8.6

Use a 4 point moving average to predict the temperature for Spring and Summer of Year 3.

Solution

(a) $1st\ moving\ average\ =\ \dfrac{12.1 + 18.6 + 11.2 + 8.1}{4}$

$$=\ 12.5$$

$2nd\ moving\ average\ =\ \dfrac{18.6 + 11.2 + 8.1 + 12.4}{4}$

$$=\ 12.575$$

$3rd\ moving\ average\ =\ \dfrac{11.2 + 8.1 + 12.4 + 19}{4}$

$$=\ 12.675$$

$$\text{4th moving average} = \frac{8.1 + 12.4 + 19 + 11.8}{4}$$
$$= 12.825$$

$$\text{5th moving average} = \frac{12.4 + 19 + 11.8 + 8.6}{4}$$
$$= 12.95$$

The differences between the moving averages are

$$0.075, \quad 0.1, \quad 0.15, \quad 0.125$$

$$\text{The mean difference} = \frac{0.075 + 0.1 + 0.15 + 0.125}{4}$$
$$= 0.1125$$

We can now predict:

$$\text{6th moving average} = 12.95 + 0.1125$$
$$= 13.0625$$

$$\text{7th moving average} = 13.0625 + 0.1125$$
$$= 13.175$$

$$\text{Year 3 } \textit{Spring} \text{ temperature} = 13.0625 \times 4 - 8.6 - 11.8 - 19.0$$
$$= 12.85$$

$$\text{Year 3 } \textit{Summer} \text{ temperature} = 13.175 \times 4 - 12.85 - 8.6 - 11.8$$
$$= 19.45$$

Exercises

1. (a) Calculate the 3 point moving averages for this set of data:

    $$4 \quad 3 \quad 5 \quad 4 \quad 3 \quad 5$$

   (b) What do you notice about the moving averages?

2. (a) Calculate the 4 point moving averages for this set of data:

    $$6 \quad 2 \quad 7 \quad 1 \quad 8 \quad 4 \quad 9 \quad 3 \quad 10$$

   (b) Describe what is happening to the moving average.

   (c) Predict the next *two* values using a 4 point moving average.

3.   (a)   Calculate the 4 point moving averages for this data:

                16   7   20   5   14.2   7.2   19.2   4.2

  (b)   Use your results to predict the next 2 values.

4.   Use a 3 point moving average to estimate the next 2 entries in this list:

                4   6   5   5.5   7.5   6.5   . . .   . . .

5.   The first value from a list of data is missing:

                ☐   3.8   6.2   5.8   4.6   4.2   6.6   6.2

  (a)   Calculate the 4 point moving averages for the data given.

  (b)   Estimate the missing value.

6.   The sales of an ice-cream company are given in the table below, in thousands of ice-creams:

1996				1997			
Spring	Summer	Autumn	Winter	Spring	Summer	Autumn	Winter
3.6	9.7	3.2	4.1	3.6	9.8	3.4	4.4

Use a 4 point moving average to estimate the number of ice-creams sold each season in 1998.

7.   The value, in pence, of a single share in a company is given in the table below:

1997				1998			
January	April	July	October	January	April	July	October
58	62	74	81	67	70	81	89

Use a 4 point moving average to estimate the value of the share for January, April, July and October 1999.

8.   A company keeps a record of its total profits, in £10 000's, for the first, second, third and fourth quarters of each year.

1997				1998			
1st	2nd	3rd	4th	1st	2nd	3rd	4th
24.1	26.3	28.4	20.4	29.3	31.9	35.2	28.4

Use a 4 point moving average to estimate the profits for:

(a)   1999,   (b)   1996.

9. A school tuck shop keeps a record of the number of cans of drink it sells over a 3-week period.

Week 1					Week 2					Week 3				
Mon	Tues	Wed	Thurs	Fri	Mon	Tues	Wed	Thurs	Fri	Mon	Tues	Wed	Thurs	Fri
18	22	9	7	15	19	23	9	8	16	21	23	10	10	16

Use a 5 point moving average to estimate the sales of cans for week 4.

10. The amount of fuel used in a school in the 4 seasons is shown in the table below (in 1000s of litres).

1997				1998			
Spring	Summer	Autumn	Winter	Spring	Summer	Autumn	Winter
5.3	4.4	5.4	7.3	6.6	5.6	6.5	8.3

Use an appropriate moving average to estimate the amount of fuel used each season in 1999.

19 Scale Drawing

19.1 Measuring Lengths

In this section we consider which units to use when measuring lengths, estimating lengths, and the errors made when measuring.

1 cm	=	10 mm
1 m	=	100 cm
1 km	=	1000 m

Example 1

Which unit of length is the most appropriate to measure:

(a)   your height,

(b)   the height of a block of flats,

(c)   the length of your foot,

(d)   the thickness of your maths book,

(e)   the distance between your school and the nearest other school?

Solution

(a)   cm

(b)   m

(c)   cm

(d)   mm

(e)   probably km

Example 2

Estimate the lengths of each of the following:

(a)   a car,

(b)   the width of your thumbnail,

(c)   the length of your pen.

Solution

(a)   This will depend on the type of car, but answers between 2 m and 4 m are reasonable.

(b)   Between 1 cm and $1\frac{1}{2}$ cm (or between 10 mm and 15 mm).

(c)   15 cm.

Example 3

A line is measured to the nearest centimetre as 12 cm.

(a)   What is the *shortest* possible length of the line?

(b)   What length must the actual length of the line be *less than*?

Solution

(a)   11.5 cm, as this is the shortest length that rounds to 12 cm.

(b)   12.5 cm, as this is the shortest length that rounds to 13 cm, rather than to 12 cm.

> The answers in Example 3 are called
> *upper* and *lower bounds*

Note: the answer to Example 3 (a) is called the *lower bound* of the length;
the answer to Example 3 (b) is called the *upper bound*.

Exercises

1.   Which unit of length would be the most appropriate if you were measuring:

(a)   the distance between two towns,

(b)   the height of your classroom,

(c)   the length of a calculator,

(d)   the thickness of a dictionary,

(e)   the height of your desk?

2.   Choosing suitable units estimate the following distances:

(a)   the length of your classroom,

(b)   the height of your teacher,

(c)   the height of your classroom,

(d)   the length of your little finger,

(e)   the width of your desk.

3.   Are each of the following statements likely to be *true* or *false*?

      (a)   John's height is 242 cm.

      (b)   The height of a desk is 1.2 m.

      (c)   The height of a door is 190 cm.

      (d)   The length of a football pitch is 800 m.

      (e)   The length of a finger is 8 cm.

      (f)   The thickness of a sheet of paper is 1 mm.

4.   The length of a line is measured as 10 cm, to the nearest cm. What are the upper and lower bounds of its actual length?

5.   The length of a pen is measured as 16 cm, to the nearest cm. What is the minimum possible length of the pen?

6.   The distance between 2 airports is 1700 km, correct to the nearest 100 km.

      (a)   What are the upper and lower bounds of the actual distance?

      (b)   What would be your answers to (a) if the information was correct to the nearest 10 km?

7.   The end of Andy's tape measure is broken, and all the distances that he measures are 1 cm shorter than he thinks. Is this error significant when he measures:

      (a)   5 cm,   (b)   5 m,

      (c)   20 cm,   (d)   1 m?

8.   (a)   Estimate the lengths of each of these lines to the nearest cm:

             (i)   ——————————————————————————

             (ii)   ——————————

             (iii) ———————————————

             (iv)   ————————————————————————

             (v)   ——————————————————————————

             (vi)   ————————————————————————————————

      (b)   Measure the lengths of each line, correct to the nearest cm.

      (c)   Explain why you would get more sensible results if you measured the lines to the nearest mm.

9. (a) Estimate the size of each of these angles:

    (i)

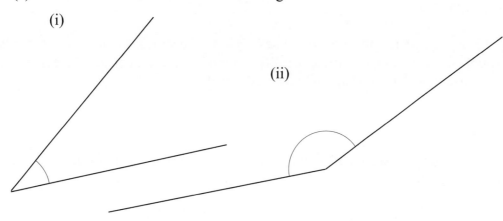

    (ii)

    (iii)

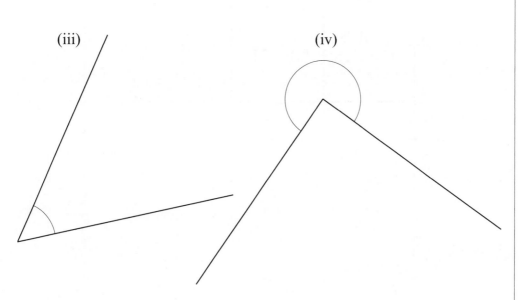

    (iv)

    (b) Measure the size of each angle to see how good your estimates were.

10. (a) Measure the 3 angles in this triangle:

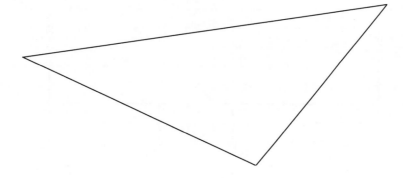

    (b) Check that they add up to 180 °.

19.2 Plans

Plans are drawn using a scale such as 1 : 100. This means that 1 cm on the plan represents 100 cm, or 1 m, in real life. In this section we consider how to take measurements from plans and how to draw plans.

Example 1

The diagram shows the plan of a village hall, on a scale of 1 : 100.

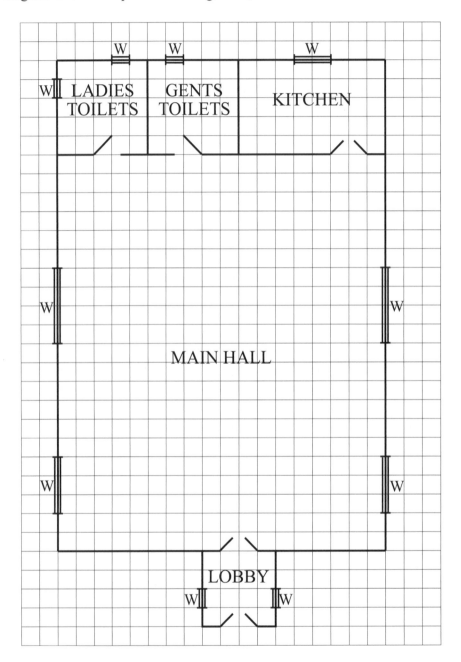

What are the 'real life' measurements for:

(a)   the dimensions of the kitchen,

(b)   the dimensions of the gents toilet,

(c)   the length of the main hall,

(d)   the area of the lobby,

(e)   the length of the kitchen window?

Solution

(a)   On the plan the kitchen is 4 cm by 2.5 cm. In reality these distances are 100 times larger, that is, $4 \times 100 = 400$ cm by $2.5 \times 100 = 250$ cm, or 4 m by 2.5 m.

(b)   On the plan the gents toilet is 2.5 cm by 2.5 cm. In reality it is 250 cm by 250 cm, or 2.5 m by 2.5 m.

(c)   The length of the main hall is 10.5 cm on the plan. In reality it will be 1050 cm, or 10.5 m.

(d)   On the plan the lobby is 2 cm by 2 cm. This corresponds to actual dimensions of 2 m by 2 m, so

$$\text{area} = 2 \times 2$$

$$= 4 \text{ m}^2$$

(e)   The length of this window on the plan is 1 cm. The actual length will be 100 cm, or 1 m.

Example 2

Veronica makes a rough sketch of her bedroom and measures the lengths of the walls.

Draw an accurate plan of Veronica's bedroom, using a scale of 1 : 50.

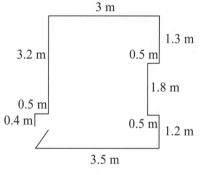

Solution

A scale of 1 : 50 means that 1 cm on the plan will represent an actual distance of 50 cm.

All the distances on the sketch must be divided by 50 to find the distances that should be used on the plan.

The table shows these distances:

Actual Size in		Size on Plan in
m	cm	cm
3	300	$300 \div 50 = 6$
1.3	130	$130 \div 50 = 2.6$
1.8	180	$180 \div 50 = 3.6$
1.2	120	$120 \div 50 = 2.4$
3.5	350	$350 \div 50 = 7$
0.4	40	$40 \div 50 = 0.8$
0.5	50	$50 \div 50 = 1$
3.2	320	$320 \div 50 = 6.4$

The plan can then be drawn accurately, as shown in the diagram.

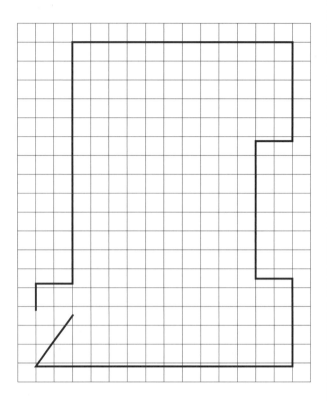

 Exercises

1. This is a plan of a temporary building at a school. It is drawn using a scale of 1 : 100.

   What are the actual measurements of:

   (a) the length of the classroom,

   (b) the width of the classroom,

   (c) the dimensions of the lobby,

   (d) the dimensions of the store?

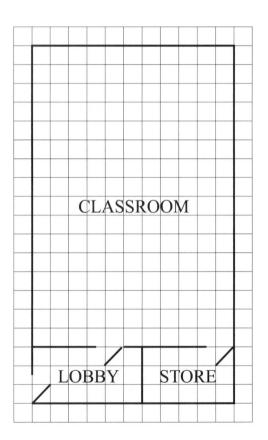

2. Adam draws a plan of his bedroom using a scale of 1 : 200. Find the actual lengths of the walls in his bedroom.

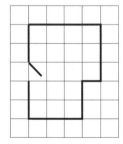

3.   Jai's garage is 3 m wide and 8 m long. What would be the dimensions of this garage on a plan with a scale of:

 (a)   1 to 100,

 (b)   1 to 200,

 (c)   1 to 50,

 (d)   1 to 10,

 (e)   1 to 20?

4.   On a plan with a scale of 1 : 50, the floor of a rectangular cupboard is shown with dimensions 2.5 cm by 3.6 cm. What are the actual dimensions of the floor? Give your answers in metres.

5.   Alice draws this sketch of her bedroom.

 The doorway is 0.7 m wide.

 (a)   Draw a plan of this room using a scale of 1 : 50.

 (b)   Calculate the actual length of the wall that is *not* at right angles to the other walls.

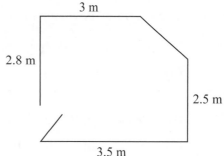

6.   On a plan, an actual length of 5 m is represented by 25 cm. What is the scale of the plan?

7.   A rectangular room has dimensions 4 cm by 5 cm on a plan with a scale of 1 : 120.

 (a)   What are the actual dimensions of the room in metres?

 (b)   What is the floor area of the room?

 (c)   What is the length of the longest straight line that could be drawn on the floor of the room?

8.   This diagram shows the plan of a room, drawn using a scale of 1 : 200.

 Calculate:

 (a)   the perimeter of the room,

 (b)   the total floor area of the room,

 (c)   the length of the longest straight line that could be drawn on the floor of the room.

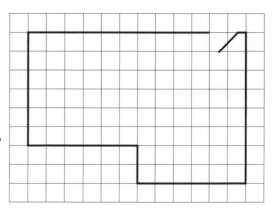

9. The diagram shows the plan of
   the ground floor of a house, using
   a scale of 1 : 120.

   Calculate the following:

   (a) the total length of the two
       windows in the lounge/diner,

   (b) the floor area of the kitchen,

   (c) the total floor area of the
       lounge/diner,

   (d) the floor area of the hall,
       excluding the stairs.

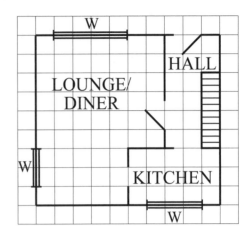

10. The diagram shows the plan of a workshop.

    The area of the workshop floor is 72 m^2.

    (a) What actual area does each small
        square on the grid represent?

    (b) What length does 5 mm on the plan represent?

    (c) What is the scale of the plan?

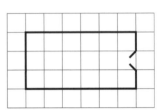

19.3 Maps

Scales are used on maps in the same way that they are used in plans. A scale of
1 : 50 000 is used on many Ordnance Survey maps. This means that 1 cm on the
map represents an actual distance of 50 000 cm (or 500 m or 0.5 km).

Example 1

This map shows roads linking 3 towns
and is drawn using a scale of 1 : 300 000.

What is the actual distance on a
straight line between:

(a) Buxton and Ashbourne,

(b) Buxton and Leek?

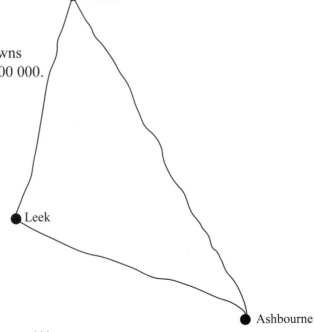

Solution

(a)   The distance between Buxton and Ashbourne is 9.8 cm on the map.

Actual distance   = 9.8 × 300 000

= 2 940 000 cm

= 29 400 m

= 29.4 km

(b)   The distance between Buxton and Leek on the map is 6.1 cm.

Actual distance   = 6.1 × 300 000

= 1 830 000 cm

= 18.3 km

Example 2

The distance between two towns is 3.5 km. How far apart would these towns be on a map with a scale of 1 : 50 000 ?

Solution

Actual distance   = 3.5 km

= 3500 m

= 350 000 cm

Distance on map $= \dfrac{350\ 000}{50\ 000}$

= 7 cm

Alternative solution: a scale of 1 : 50 000 means that 1 cm on the map represents 50 000 cm or 500 m or 0.5 km, in reality.

Distance on map $= \dfrac{3.5}{0.5}$

= 7 cm

Exercises

1.   The following map shows some places in Kent and is drawn using a scale of 1 : 300 000.

What is the actual distance on a straight line, in km, between:

(a)   Canterbury and Dover,

(b)   Whitstable and Margate,

(c)   Sandwich and Deal,

(d)   Herne Bay and Folkstone?

19.3

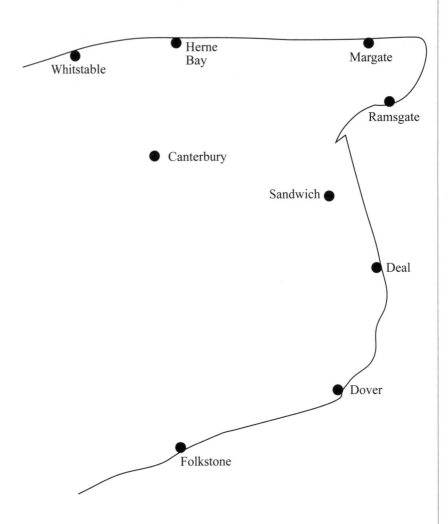

2.   The map below shows a small island drawn using a scale of 1 : 25 000.
      There are three lookout posts, at A, B and C.

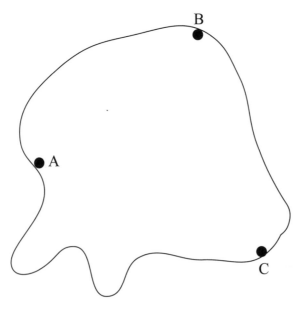

A person walks from A to B, from B to C, and from C back to A. He always
walks in a straight line between the lookout posts. What is the total distance
that the person walks?

3. A map has a scale of 1 : 50 000. What are the actual distances, in km, that are represented by each of these lengths on the map:

   (a) 4 cm,

   (b) 10 cm,

   (c) 3.2 cm,

   (d) 5.1 cm?

4. The distance between two places on a map is 6 cm. If the map has a scale of 1 : 40 000, what is the actual distance between the two places?

5. On a map with a scale of 1 : 3 000 000, the distance between Edinburgh and London is 18 cm. What is the actual distance, in km, between these cities?

6. Two towns are 15 km apart. What would be the distance between the two towns on a map with a scale of 1 : 300 000?

7. A tower is 2 km due north of a church. A windmill is 5 km east of the tower.

   Tower ●   ● Windmill

   Church ●

   A map is to be drawn with a scale of 1 : 25 000.

   (a) What will be the distance on the map between the church and the tower?

   (b) What will be the distance on the map between the tower and the windmill?

   (c) Draw the map, and use it to calculate the actual distance between the church and the windmill.

8. The distance between London and Birmingham is 165 km. What would be the distance between these two cities on a map with a scale of:

   (a) 1 : 500 000,

   (b) 1 : 1 000 000,

   (c) 1 : 300 000,

   (d) 1 : 110 000 ?

9.   A student measures the distances between various points shown in her school grounds. The points are shown in the diagram, which is *not* drawn to scale.

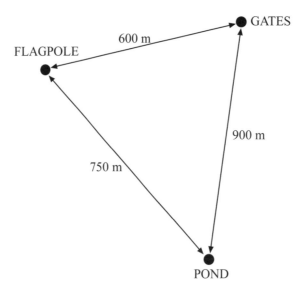

(a)   Draw a map to show this information, using a scale of 1 : 10 000.

(b)   A person is exactly halfway between the gates and the pond. How far are they from the flagpole?

(c)   Another student stands at the gates looking towards the flagpole. They turn anticlockwise so that they are looking at the pond. What angle does the student turn through?

10.   On a map, a distance of 40 km, is represented by 32 cm. What actual distance would be represented by 14 cm on the map?

11.   A map has a scale of 1 : 50 000. A park is shown on the map as a rectangle measuring 6 cm by 4.2 cm. What is the actual area of the park?

20 | Arithmetic: Fractions

20.1 | Revision: Whole Numbers and Decimals

In this section we revise *addition, subtraction, multiplication* and *division* of whole numbers and decimals, before starting to work with *fractions*.

Example 1

Calculate:

(a) $18 + 49$

(b) $1.6 + 0.84$

(c) $3.82 - 1.6$

Solution

(a)
$$\begin{array}{r} 18 \\ + \ 49 \\ \hline 67 \\ \hline \end{array}$$

(b)
$$\begin{array}{r} 1.60 \\ + \ 0.84 \\ \hline 2.44 \\ \hline \end{array}$$

(c)
$$\begin{array}{r} 3.82 \\ - \ 1.60 \\ \hline 2.22 \\ \hline \end{array}$$

Example 2

Calculate:

(a) 18×34

(b) 1.7×2.6

Solution

(a)
$$\begin{array}{r} 18 \\ \times \ 34 \\ \hline 72 \\ 540 \\ \hline 612 \\ \hline \end{array}$$

(b)
$$\begin{array}{r} 17 \\ \times \ 26 \\ \hline 102 \\ 340 \\ \hline 442 \\ \hline \end{array}$$

Hence $1.7 \times 1.6 = 4.42$

Example 3

Calculate:

(a) $165 \div 5$

(b) $4.26 \div 3$

Solution

(a)
$$\begin{array}{r} 33 \\ 5 \overline{)16^{1}5} \end{array}$$

so $165 \div 5 = 33$

(b)
$$\begin{array}{r} 1.42 \\ 3 \overline{)4.^{1}26} \end{array}$$

so $4.26 \div 3 = 1.42$

Exercises

1. Calculate:

   (a) 182 + 57   (b) 32 + 168   (c) 1807 + 94

   (d) 3.2 + 4.7   (e) 18.2 + 1.9   (f) 3.71 + 4.2

   (g) 0.26 + 1.2   (h) 11.4 + 6.21   (i) 0.09 + 0.123

   (j) 38 + 4.7   (k) 0.71 + 2.8   (l) 4.52 + 9.89

2. Calculate:

   (a) 192 − 71   (b) 486 − 234   (c) 620 − 108

   (d) 0.9 − 0.2   (e) 1.8 − 0.3   (f) 2.42 − 1.23

   (g) 0.8 − 0.11   (h) 8.9 − 1.12   (i) 3.7 − 2.15

   (j) 28 − 3.7   (k) 52 − 6.9   (l) 4.07 − 3.88

3. Calculate:

   (a) 18×3 (b) 42×5 (c) 63×7

   (d) 12×15 (e) 26×14 (f) 39×23

   (g) 0.7×5 (h) 1.9×6 (i) 4.29×3

   (j) 1.8×2.9 (k) 3.5×2.6 (l) 1.42×1.6

4. Calculate:

   (a) $468 \div 2$ (b) $578 \div 2$ (c) $145 \div 5$

   (d) $345 \div 5$ (e) $78 \div 3$ (f) $981 \div 3$

   (g) $6.84 \div 4$ (h) $14.7 \div 7$ (i) $7.92 \div 6$

5. There were 52 people on a bus and 17 got off. How many people were still on the bus?

6. Floppy disks cost 34p each. How much would 6 floppy disks cost?

7. It costs £5.20 for one adult to go into a theme park. How much would it cost in total for 24 adults to go into the theme park?

8. Tickets for a show cost £3 each. To cover the cost of putting on the show, £378 is needed. How many tickets must be sold to cover the cost of the show?

9. An 8 m length of rope is cut into 5 pieces of equal length. How long is each of the 5 pieces?

10. A PE department has £30 to spend on footballs which cost £4 each.

    (a) How many footballs can they buy?

    (b) How much money will they have left?

20.2 Addition and Subtraction of Fractions

In this section we consider how to add and subtract fractions. The key step in this process is to make sure that both fractions have the *same denominator*.

Example 1

Calculate:

(a) $\dfrac{1}{5} + \dfrac{2}{5}$

(b) $\dfrac{5}{6} - \dfrac{1}{6}$

Solution

(a) As the denominator is the same in both fractions, we simply add the numbers on the top of the fraction to give

$$\frac{1}{5} + \frac{2}{5} = \frac{1+2}{5}$$

$$= \frac{3}{5}$$

This addition is shown in the diagram below:

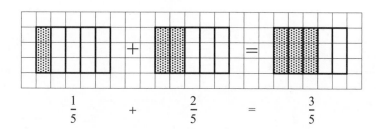

(b) The denominator is the same in both fractions, so

$$\frac{5}{6} - \frac{1}{6} = \frac{5-1}{6}$$

$$= \frac{4}{6}$$

$$= \frac{2}{3}$$

This is shown in the diagram below:

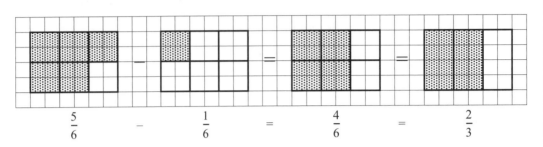

$$\frac{5}{6} \quad - \quad \frac{1}{6} \quad = \quad \frac{4}{6} \quad = \quad \frac{2}{3}$$

Example 2

Calculate:

(a) $\frac{1}{4} + \frac{2}{5}$

(b) $\frac{2}{3} - \frac{1}{4}$

Solution

(a) These fractions do not have the same denominator, so the first step is to change them so that they do. In this case, we can use 20 as the common denominator.

$$\frac{1}{4} + \frac{2}{5} \quad = \quad \frac{5}{20} + \frac{8}{20}$$

$$= \quad \frac{5 + 8}{20}$$

$$= \quad \frac{13}{20}$$

This is illustrated in the diagram below:

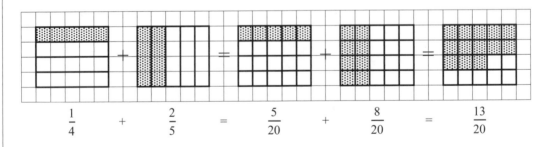

$$\frac{1}{4} \quad + \quad \frac{2}{5} \quad = \quad \frac{5}{20} \quad + \quad \frac{8}{20} \quad = \quad \frac{13}{20}$$

(b) In this case we can use a common denominator of 12.

$$\frac{2}{3} - \frac{1}{4} \quad = \quad \frac{8}{12} - \frac{3}{12}$$

$$= \quad \frac{8 - 3}{12}$$

$$= \quad \frac{5}{12}$$

This is illustrated in the diagram below:

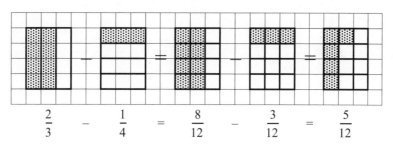

$$\frac{2}{3} \quad - \quad \frac{1}{4} \quad = \quad \frac{8}{12} \quad - \quad \frac{3}{12} \quad = \quad \frac{5}{12}$$

Example 3

Calculate:

(a) $1\frac{1}{8} + 3\frac{1}{3}$ (b) $4\frac{3}{8} - 1\frac{3}{4}$ (c) $2\frac{2}{3} + 1\frac{1}{2}$

Solution

(a) $1 + 3 \ = 4$

$$\frac{1}{8} + \frac{1}{3} = \frac{3}{24} + \frac{8}{24}$$

$$= \frac{3 + 8}{24}$$

$$= \frac{11}{24}$$

So $1\frac{1}{8} + 3\frac{1}{3} = 4\frac{11}{24}$

(b) $4\frac{3}{8} - 1\frac{3}{4} \ = \ \frac{35}{8} - \frac{7}{4}$

$$= \frac{35}{8} - \frac{14}{8}$$

$$= \frac{35 - 14}{8}$$

$$= \frac{21}{8}$$

$$= 2\frac{5}{8}$$

Note: It is usually easier to convert the mixed numbers into improper fractions.

(c) $2\dfrac{2}{3}+1\dfrac{1}{2}$ $=\dfrac{8}{3}+\dfrac{3}{2}$

$=\dfrac{16}{6}+\dfrac{9}{6}$

$=\dfrac{16+9}{6}$

$=\dfrac{25}{6}$

$=4\dfrac{1}{6}$

Exercises

1. Calculate:

(a) $\dfrac{3}{7}+\dfrac{1}{7}$

(b) $\dfrac{3}{8}+\dfrac{1}{8}$

(c) $\dfrac{1}{9}+\dfrac{7}{9}$

(d) $\dfrac{3}{10}+\dfrac{7}{10}$

(e) $\dfrac{1}{5}+\dfrac{3}{5}$

(f) $\dfrac{2}{7}+\dfrac{4}{7}$

(g) $\dfrac{1}{4}+\dfrac{3}{4}$

(h) $\dfrac{5}{8}-\dfrac{3}{8}$

(i) $\dfrac{7}{9}-\dfrac{5}{9}$

(j) $\dfrac{9}{10}-\dfrac{7}{10}$

(k) $\dfrac{8}{11}-\dfrac{3}{11}$

(l) $\dfrac{4}{15}-\dfrac{2}{15}$

(m) $\dfrac{6}{13}-\dfrac{3}{13}$

(n) $\dfrac{4}{7}-\dfrac{3}{7}$

(o) $\dfrac{6}{25}-\dfrac{2}{25}$

2. Fill in the missing numbers:

(a) $\dfrac{1}{2}+\dfrac{1}{5}=\dfrac{?}{10}+\dfrac{?}{10}=\dfrac{?}{10}$

(b) $\dfrac{4}{5}+\dfrac{2}{3}=\dfrac{?}{15}+\dfrac{?}{15}=\dfrac{?}{15}$

(c) $\dfrac{1}{6}+\dfrac{4}{5}=\dfrac{5}{?}+\dfrac{24}{?}=\dfrac{?}{?}$

(d) $\dfrac{4}{7}-\dfrac{1}{3}=\dfrac{?}{21}-\dfrac{?}{21}=\dfrac{?}{21}$

(e) $\dfrac{5}{6}-\dfrac{2}{3}=\dfrac{5}{6}-\dfrac{?}{6}=\dfrac{?}{6}$

3. Calculate:

   (a) $\dfrac{1}{3} + \dfrac{1}{2}$

   (b) $\dfrac{3}{4} + \dfrac{2}{3}$

   (c) $\dfrac{1}{5} + \dfrac{1}{4}$

   (d) $\dfrac{3}{5} + \dfrac{2}{3}$

   (e) $\dfrac{5}{8} + \dfrac{1}{4}$

   (f) $\dfrac{1}{3} + \dfrac{1}{6}$

   (g) $\dfrac{4}{5} + \dfrac{2}{7}$

   (h) $\dfrac{1}{7} + \dfrac{2}{3}$

   (i) $\dfrac{1}{2} + \dfrac{1}{10}$

   (j) $\dfrac{6}{7} + \dfrac{2}{3}$

   (k) $\dfrac{5}{6} - \dfrac{1}{2}$

   (l) $\dfrac{7}{8} - \dfrac{3}{4}$

   (m) $\dfrac{8}{9} - \dfrac{3}{4}$

   (n) $\dfrac{3}{7} - \dfrac{1}{3}$

   (o) $\dfrac{4}{5} - \dfrac{3}{4}$

4. A birthday cake is divided into 12 equal parts. Andrew eats $\dfrac{3}{12}$ of the cake and Timothy eats $\dfrac{1}{12}$ of the cake.

   (a) What fraction of the cake is left?

   (b) How many pieces of cake are left?

5. A garden has an area of $\dfrac{3}{4}$ hectare. The owner buys an extra $\dfrac{3}{5}$ of a hectare of land.

   (a) What is the area of the garden now?

   (b) How much more land would the owner need to have a garden with an area of 2 hectares?

6. Steve and Sheila buy a computer. Steve fills $\dfrac{2}{5}$ of the hard disk with his programs. Sheila fills $\dfrac{1}{3}$ of the hard disk with her programs.

   (a) What fraction of the hard disk is full?

   (b) What fraction of the hard disk is empty?

   (c) Steve deletes one of his programs that takes up $\dfrac{1}{10}$ of the hard disk. What fraction of the hard disk do his programs fill now?

7. If $\dfrac{9}{10}$ of all men in the UK own cars, and $\dfrac{2}{3}$ of all men in the UK own *more than one* car, what fraction of men in the UK:

   (a) do *not* own a car,

   (b) own only *one* car?

8. Calculate:

(a) $1\frac{1}{2} + 1\frac{1}{3}$

(b) $1\frac{3}{4} + 2\frac{1}{2}$

(c) $4\frac{2}{5} + 3\frac{1}{2}$

(d) $1\frac{4}{7} + 1\frac{3}{8}$

(e) $1\frac{1}{2} - \frac{2}{3}$

(f) $3\frac{1}{4} - 1\frac{3}{5}$

(g) $2\frac{1}{2} - 1\frac{5}{8}$

(h) $4\frac{1}{7} + 3\frac{2}{3}$

(i) $4\frac{3}{5} - 2\frac{7}{8}$

(j) $6\frac{1}{4} - 1\frac{2}{5}$

(k) $3\frac{1}{2} - 1\frac{3}{4}$

(l) $5\frac{1}{4} - 2\frac{1}{2}$

9. Ron wins $£1\frac{1}{4}$ million. He gives $£\frac{3}{5}$ million to his daughter and $£\frac{1}{3}$ million to his wife. How much does he have left?

10. An old-fashioned gardener measures the height of a plant as $6\frac{3}{8}$ inches. A week later the height is measured as $8\frac{3}{5}$ inches. How much did the plant grow during the week?

20.3 Multiplying Fractions

In this section we extend the ideas of Unit 10, where you multiplied fractions by numbers, to now include multiplying fractions by fractions.

Example 1

Calculate:

(a) $\frac{1}{3}$ of £24,

(b) $\frac{2}{5}$ of £40,

(c) $\frac{3}{7}$ of 35 m.

Solution

(a) $\frac{1}{3}$ of £24 $= \frac{24}{3}$

$= £8$

(b) $\dfrac{1}{5}$ of £40 $= \dfrac{40}{5}$

$= £8$

$\dfrac{2}{5}$ of £40 $= 2 \times 8$

$= £16$

or $\dfrac{2}{5}$ of £40 $= \dfrac{2 \times 40}{5}$

$= \dfrac{80}{5}$

$= £16$

(c) $\dfrac{1}{7}$ of 35 m $= \dfrac{35}{7}$

$= 5$ m

$\dfrac{3}{7}$ of 35 m $= 3 \times 5$

$= 15$ m

or $\dfrac{3}{7}$ of 35 m $= \dfrac{3 \times 35}{7}$

$= \dfrac{105}{7}$

$= 15$ m

Example 2

Calculate $\dfrac{2}{5} \times \dfrac{3}{4}$ and illustrate this on a diagram.

Solution

(c) $\dfrac{2}{5} \times \dfrac{3}{4} = \dfrac{2 \times 3}{5 \times 4}$

$= \dfrac{6}{20}$

$= \dfrac{3}{10}$

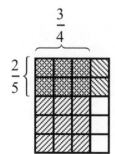

Note that 6 of the small squares are shaded twice, so $\dfrac{2}{5} \times \dfrac{3}{4} = \dfrac{6}{20} = \dfrac{3}{10}$.

Note that we are using the rule:

$$\dfrac{a}{b} \times \dfrac{c}{d} = \dfrac{a \times c}{b \times d}$$

Example 3

Calculate:

(a) $\dfrac{4}{7} \times \dfrac{3}{5}$ (b) $1\dfrac{3}{4} \times \dfrac{2}{3}$ (c) $1\dfrac{1}{2} \times 3\dfrac{1}{3}$

Solution

(a) $\dfrac{4}{7} \times \dfrac{3}{5} = \dfrac{4 \times 3}{7 \times 5}$

$= \dfrac{12}{35}$

(b) $1\dfrac{3}{4} \times \dfrac{2}{3} = \dfrac{7}{\cancel{4}_2} \times \dfrac{\cancel{2}^1}{3}$ (*Note*: it is usually quicker to cancel down at
                                                    this stage rather than at the end.)

$= \dfrac{7 \times 1}{2 \times 3}$

$= \dfrac{7}{6}$

$= 1\dfrac{1}{6}$

(c) $2\dfrac{1}{4} \times 3\dfrac{1}{3} = \dfrac{\cancel{9}^3}{\cancel{4}_2} \times \dfrac{\cancel{10}^5}{\cancel{3}_1}$

$= \dfrac{3 \times 5}{2 \times 1}$

$= \dfrac{15}{2}$

$= 7\dfrac{1}{2}$

Exercises

1. Calculate:

(a) $\frac{1}{5} \times 15$ (b) $\frac{1}{8} \times 32$ (c) $\frac{7}{8} \times 16$

(d) $\frac{3}{7} \times 14$ (e) $\frac{3}{4} \times 28$ (f) $\frac{4}{5} \times 30$

(g) $\frac{5}{7} \times 21$ (h) $24 \times \frac{5}{8}$ (i) $18 \times \frac{5}{9}$

(j) $66 \times \frac{2}{3}$ (k) $34 \times \frac{4}{17}$ (l) $\frac{5}{19} \times 57$

2. Calculate:

(a) $\frac{1}{2} \times \frac{1}{3}$ (b) $\frac{1}{2} \times \frac{1}{2}$ (c) $\frac{1}{3} \times \frac{1}{4}$

(d) $\frac{2}{3} \times \frac{3}{4}$ (e) $\frac{3}{7} \times \frac{4}{5}$ (f) $\frac{3}{8} \times \frac{3}{4}$

(g) $\frac{4}{7} \times \frac{2}{9}$ (h) $\frac{6}{7} \times \frac{3}{8}$ (i) $\frac{5}{6} \times \frac{5}{7}$.

(j) $\frac{3}{10} \times \frac{3}{7}$ (k) $\frac{1}{2} \times \frac{3}{19}$ (l) $\frac{4}{11} \times \frac{2}{3}$

3. Calculate:

(a) $1\frac{1}{2} \times \frac{3}{4}$ (b) $4\frac{1}{2} \times \frac{2}{3}$ (c) $1\frac{3}{4} \times \frac{2}{5}$

(d) $1\frac{3}{7} \times \frac{1}{2}$ (e) $4\frac{1}{4} \times \frac{1}{5}$ (f) $3\frac{1}{7} \times \frac{1}{3}$

(g) $4\frac{1}{2} \times \frac{3}{5}$ (h) $1\frac{1}{2} \times 1\frac{1}{2}$ (i) $1\frac{1}{3} \times 1\frac{1}{2}$

(j) $1\frac{1}{4} \times 2\frac{1}{2}$ (k) $3\frac{1}{4} \times 2\frac{1}{3}$ (l) $1\frac{1}{4} \times 2\frac{1}{5}$

4. Calculate the area of each of these rectangles:

(a)

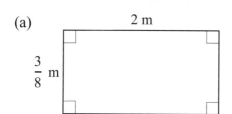

(b)

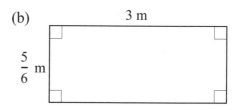

5. A cake recipe requires $\frac{3}{4}$ kg of flour. How much flour is needed to make:

    (a) 2 cakes,

    (b) 6 cakes,

    (c) 10 cakes?

6. Jan buys $\frac{3}{4}$ kg cheese. She keeps $\frac{2}{3}$ of it and gives $\frac{1}{3}$ to her sister. What is the weight of:

    (a) the cheese Jan keeps,

    (b) the cheese Jan gives to her sister?

7. A large company makes £$\frac{3}{5}$ million profit. They spend $\frac{1}{4}$ of this on new equipment.

    (a) How much does the company spend on new equipment?

    (b) How much is left?

8. Calculate the area of each of these rectangles:

    (a)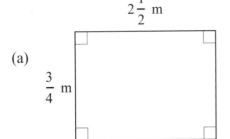

    (b)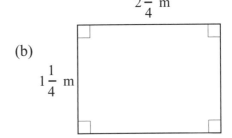

9. The diagram shows a small picture frame. The shaded border is $\frac{3}{4}$ cm wide.

    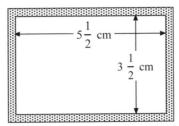

    What is the area of the shaded border?

10. A petrol can holds $3\frac{1}{2}$ litres. Sanjit fills up a lawn mower and uses $\frac{1}{3}$ of the petrol from the full can.

   (a)   How much petrol does the lawn mower hold?

   (b)   How much petrol is left in the can?

   Later, Sanjit uses another $\frac{3}{4}$ litres of petrol from the can.

   (c)   How much petrol has he now used?

20.4 Dividing Fractions

In this section we consider how to divide fractions and whole numbers by either whole numbers or fractions.

Example 1

Calculate $\frac{1}{4} \div 3$.

Solution

You can deal with this problem by thinking about the fraction being divided into 3 parts.

$\frac{1}{4}$ of the diagram has been divided into 3 parts:

$\left.\right\}$ *Divided into 3 parts*

Each of these parts is $\frac{1}{12}$ of the whole, so

$$\frac{1}{4} \div 3 = \frac{1}{12}$$

We can also obtain the result in this way:

$$\frac{1}{4} \div 3 = \frac{1}{4} \times \frac{1}{3}$$

$$= \frac{1}{12}$$

which uses the rule:

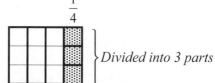

$$\frac{a}{b} \div c = \frac{a}{b} \times \frac{1}{c}$$

Example 2

Calculate: (a) $4 \div \dfrac{1}{3}$,   (b) $4 \div \dfrac{2}{5}$.

Solution

(a)   The problem is to calculate how many $\dfrac{1}{3}$s there are in 4 whole units. The

four whole units are shown below, and each is divided into $\dfrac{1}{3}$s.

The diagram shows 12 $\dfrac{1}{3}$s, so

$$4 \div \frac{1}{3} \ = \ 12$$

We can obtain this result from

$$4 \div \frac{1}{3} \ = \ 4 \times 3$$

$$= \ 12$$

(b)   The problem is to calculate how many $\dfrac{2}{5}$s there are in 4 whole units.

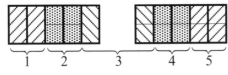 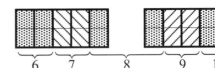

The diagram shows 10 $\dfrac{2}{5}$s, so

$$4 \div \frac{2}{5} \ = \ 10$$

We can also obtain this result from

$$4 \div \frac{2}{5} \ = \ 4 \times \frac{5}{2}$$

$$= \ \frac{20}{2}$$

$$= \ 10$$

using the rule: $\boxed{\ a \div \dfrac{b}{c} \ = \ \dfrac{a \times c}{b}\ }$

Example 3

Calculate: (a) $\dfrac{3}{4} \div \dfrac{1}{5}$ (b) $\dfrac{5}{7} \div \dfrac{2}{3}$ (c) $\dfrac{3}{4} \div \dfrac{9}{10}$

Solution

These problems can be tackled using the same approach as when a whole number is divided by a fraction.

(a) $\dfrac{3}{4} \div \dfrac{1}{5} = \dfrac{3}{4} \times \dfrac{5}{1}$

           $= \dfrac{15}{4}$

           $= 3\dfrac{3}{4}$

(b) $\dfrac{5}{7} \div \dfrac{2}{3} = \dfrac{5}{7} \times \dfrac{3}{2}$

           $= \dfrac{15}{14}$

           $= 1\dfrac{1}{14}$

(c) $\dfrac{3}{4} \div \dfrac{9}{10} = \dfrac{\overset{1}{\cancel{3}}}{\underset{2}{\cancel{4}}} \times \dfrac{\overset{5}{\cancel{10}}}{\underset{3}{\cancel{9}}}$ [*Note:* You can cancel *only* when the 2nd fraction has been turned upside-down.]

           $= \dfrac{5}{6}$

We are using the rule:

$$\dfrac{a}{b} \div \dfrac{c}{d} = \dfrac{a}{b} \times \dfrac{d}{c}$$

Exercises

1.   Calculate:

    (a) $\dfrac{1}{2} \div 3$ (b) $\dfrac{3}{4} \div 2$ (c) $\dfrac{1}{8} \div 2$

    (d) $\dfrac{3}{4} \div 4$ (e) $\dfrac{5}{8} \div 3$ (f) $\dfrac{4}{5} \div 2$

    (g) $\dfrac{6}{7} \div 3$ (h) $\dfrac{4}{5} \div 9$ (i) $\dfrac{1}{8} \div 3$

(j) $\dfrac{5}{6} \div 4$ (k) $\dfrac{9}{10} \div 6$ (l) $\dfrac{4}{5} \div 7$

2. Calculate:

(a) $6 \div \dfrac{1}{2}$ (b) $9 \div \dfrac{1}{3}$ (c) $8 \div \dfrac{1}{3}$

(d) $2 \div \dfrac{1}{4}$ (e) $5 \div \dfrac{2}{3}$ (f) $4 \div \dfrac{3}{4}$

(g) $8 \div \dfrac{1}{7}$ (h) $5 \div \dfrac{5}{7}$ (i) $9 \div \dfrac{3}{7}$

(j) $6 \div \dfrac{2}{3}$ (k) $14 \div \dfrac{7}{9}$ (l) $11 \div \dfrac{1}{13}$

3. Calculate:

(a) $\dfrac{1}{2} \div \dfrac{1}{3}$ (b) $\dfrac{3}{8} \div \dfrac{1}{2}$ (c) $\dfrac{3}{4} \div \dfrac{2}{3}$

(d) $\dfrac{4}{5} \div \dfrac{2}{3}$ (e) $\dfrac{3}{4} \div \dfrac{1}{8}$ (f) $\dfrac{3}{8} \div \dfrac{1}{2}$

(g) $\dfrac{5}{7} \div \dfrac{2}{5}$ (h) $\dfrac{5}{7} \div \dfrac{5}{9}$ (i) $\dfrac{1}{8} \div \dfrac{2}{9}$

(j) $\dfrac{3}{4} \div \dfrac{1}{9}$ (k) $\dfrac{1}{7} \div \dfrac{1}{3}$ (l) $\dfrac{4}{5} \div \dfrac{5}{8}$

4. By using *improper fractions*, calculate:

(a) $1\dfrac{1}{2} \div 3\dfrac{1}{4}$ (b) $3\dfrac{1}{2} \div 1\dfrac{1}{4}$ (c) $1\dfrac{5}{8} \div \dfrac{5}{7}$

(d) $3\dfrac{1}{2} \div 1\dfrac{1}{2}$ (e) $5\dfrac{1}{2} \div \dfrac{2}{3}$ (f) $4\dfrac{1}{5} \div \dfrac{5}{7}$

5. Ahmed has $\dfrac{3}{4}$ kg of sweets. He divides these into 3 equal parts so that he can share them with his two brothers. What fraction of a kg does each boy get?

6. Sandra has $\dfrac{1}{4}$ litre of orange squash to make 10 drinks. How much orange squash should she put in each drink?

7. A large cake uses 3 times as much flour as a small cake. A large cake needs $1\frac{1}{8}$ kg of flour. How much flour does a small cake need?

8. A piece of leather is 20 cm wide and 45 cm long.

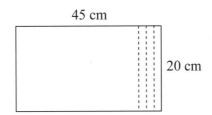

How many bookmarks, $2\frac{1}{2}$ cm wide, can be made if the leather is:

    (a) cut as shown above, to make bookmarks 20 cm long,

    (b) cut the other way to make bookmarks 45 cm long?

9. A recipe for a cake requires $\frac{1}{4}$ kg of sugar. How many cakes can be made with:

    (a) $1\frac{1}{4}$ kg of sugar.,

    (b) $2\frac{3}{4}$ kg of sugar,

    (c) $3\frac{1}{3}$ kg of sugar?

10. A car uses $1\frac{1}{4}$ litres of petrol for every 10 miles it travels. How far can the car travel on:

    (a) 5 litres of petrol,

    (b) $7\frac{1}{2}$ litres of petrol,

    (c) 9 litres of petrol?

21 Probability of One Event

21.1 Introduction to Probability

A *probability* describes mathematically how likely it is that something will happen. We can talk about the probability that it will rain tomorrow or the probability that England will win their next football match.

Example 1

Which of the words,

certain, likely, unlikely or impossible

best describes how likely each of the events below is to take place?

(a)   It will rain tomorrow.

(b)   It will snow tomorrow.

(c)   Manchester United will win the next FA Cup.

(d)   Exeter City will win the next FA Cup.

(e)   It is your teacher's birthday tomorrow.

(f)   You will obtain a 7 when rolling a dice.

Solution

(a)   This can be *likely* or *unlikely* depending on the current weather pattern.

(b)   This is *unlikely.*

(c)   This is *likely.*

(d)   This is *unlikely*, some would say *impossible*!

(e)   This is *unlikely,* but it could be true.

(f)   *Impossible* (as only numbers 1 to 6 can be obtained).

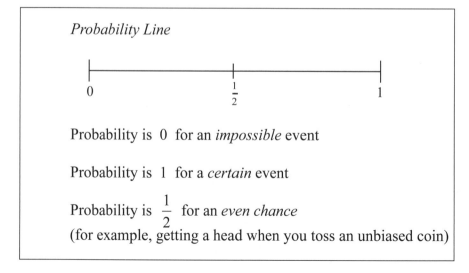

136

Example 2

For each event below, mark an estimate of the probability that it will happen on a probability scale.

(a)   It will snow on 19 August next year in London.

(b)   Your maths teacher will give you homework this week.

(c)   You will go to school tomorrow.

(d)   You will go to bed before midnight tonight.

(e)   You throw an unbiased dice and get an even number.

Solution

(a)   This is virtually impossible, so the probability will be very close to zero.

(b)   This is very likely (at least for most teachers) and so the probability will be quite high.

(c)   The answer to this depends on what day of the week it is. On a Friday or Saturday it is very unlikely that you will go to school the next day, so the probability is low.

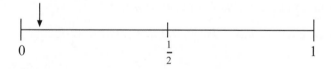

On any other day the probability is much higher as it is very likely that you will go to school the next day.

(d)   This is almost certain. The probability is very close to 1.

(e)   There are 3 even numbers and 3 odd numbers on a dice, so there is an even

chance that you will get an even number. The probability is $\frac{1}{2}$.

Exercises

1.   Use one of the words, *certain, likely, unlikely* or *impossible*, to describe
      each event below. Give a reason for each of your answers.

      (a)   You are more than 8 years old.

      (b)   You will miss the school bus tomorrow.

      (c)   Your favourite football team will win their next match.

      (d)   You will arrive at school on time tomorrow.

2.   The probability line shows the probability of 5 events, A, B, C, D and E.

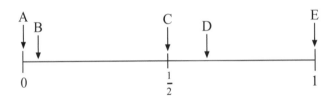

      (a)   Which event is *certain*?

      (b)   Which event is *impossible*?

      (c)   Which event is *unlikely* but *possible*?

      (d)   Which event is *most likely*, but *not certain* to occur?

3.   For each event below, draw a probability line and mark in the probability of
      the event:

      (a)   England will win the most medals at the next Olympic Games.

      (b)   You will forget to take your packed lunch to school.

      (c)   You will get a 6 when you roll an unbiased dice once.

      (d)   It will rain tomorrow.

      (e)   It will not rain tomorrow.

4.   Describe an event that is:

      (a)   impossible,   (b)   certain,

      (c)   very unlikely,   (d)   very likely.

5.   The events A, B, C and D have probabilities as shown on this probability line:

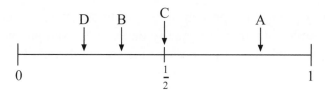

(a)   Which event is *most likely* to take place?

(b)   Which event is *most unlikely* to take place?

(c)   Which events are *more likely* to take place than event B?

(d)   Which events are *less likely* to take place than event A?

6.   (a)   What is the probability that a pupil in Year 7 will be 12 years old on their next birthday?

      (b)   What is the probability that a pupil in Year 7 will be 13 years old on their next birthday?

7.   Estimate, by marking a probability line, the probability that you will get all your next maths homework correct.

8.   The events A, B, C, D and E are listed below:

            A :   You will live to be 70 years old.

            B :   You will live to be 80 years old.

            C :   You will live to be 90 years old.

            D :   You will live to be 100 years old.

            E :   You will live to be 110 years old.

      Mark an estimate of the probability of each event on a probability line.

9.   When you toss an unbiased coin, the probability of getting a head is $\frac{1}{2}$, because you have an equal (or even) chance of getting a head or a tail. What other events have a probability of $\frac{1}{2}$?

10.   Make a list of some events that have a probability of *more than* $\frac{1}{2}$, but that are *not certain*.

21.2 Calculating the Probability of a Single Event

In this section we calculate the probabilities of single events. We consider cases where all the possible outcomes are equally likely. For example, when you roll a fair dice you are equally likely to get *any* of the six numbers. (The words 'fair' or 'unbiased' mean that all outcomes are equally likely.)

$$\text{Probability of an event} \;=\; \frac{\text{number of successful outcomes}}{\text{total number of outcomes}}$$

Example 1

When you roll a fair dice, what is the probability of getting:

(a)   a five,

(b)   an even number,

(c)   a four or a five?

Solution

The possible outcomes when you roll a dice are the scores

$$1, \;\; 2, \;\; 3, \;\; 4, \;\; 5, \;\; 6$$

so there are 6 possible outcomes.

(a)   In this case there is only one successful outcome, that is, a 5.

$$\text{Probability of a five} \;=\; \frac{\text{number of successful outcomes}}{\text{total number of outcomes}}$$

$$=\; \frac{1}{6}$$

(b)   In this case there are 3 successful outcomes, 2, 4 or 6.

$$\text{Probability of an even number} \;=\; \frac{\text{number of successful outcomes}}{\text{total number of outcomes}}$$

$$=\; \frac{3}{6}$$

$$=\; \frac{1}{2}$$

(c)   In this case there are 2 successful outcomes, 4 or 5.

$$\text{Probability of a 4 or a 5} \;=\; \frac{\text{number of successful outcomes}}{\text{total number of outcomes}}$$

$$= \frac{2}{6}$$

$$= \frac{1}{3}$$

Example 2

A bag of sweets contains 6 mints and 4 eclairs. One sweet is taken at random from the bag. What is the probability that it is:

(a)   a mint,   (b)   an eclair?

Solution

The total number of possible outcomes is 10 as there are 10 sweets in the bag.

(a)   As there are 6 mints in the bag, there are 6 successful outcomes.

Probability of a mint $= \dfrac{\text{number of successful outcomes}}{\text{total number of outcomes}}$

$$= \frac{6}{10}$$

$$= \frac{3}{5}$$

(b)   As there are 4 eclairs, there are 4 successful outcomes.

Probability of an eclair $= \dfrac{\text{number of successful outcomes}}{\text{total number of outcomes}}$

$$= \frac{4}{10}$$

$$= \frac{2}{5}$$

Exercises

1.   When you roll a fair dice, what is the probability that you obtain:

   (a)   an odd number,

   (b)   a 2,

   (c)   a multiple of 3,

   (d)   a number less than 5,

   (e)   a number greater than 4,

   (f)   a 3 or a number less than 3?

2. A bag contains 6 red sweets and 14 blue sweets. A sweet is taken at random from the bag. What is the probability that it is:

   (a) a red sweet,
   (b) a blue sweet?

3. You toss a fair coin. What is the probability that you obtain a tail?

4. The diagram shows a spinner from a game. The black arrow spins and ends up pointing to one of the four numbers.

   What is the probability that the arrow points to:

   (a) the number 1,

   (b) an even number.

   (c) a multiple of 3?

   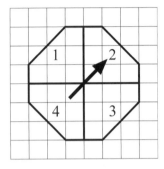

5. The diagram shows a spinner that is used in a board game. When the spinner is spun, what is the probability that it lands on:

   (a) 1,

   (b) 5,

   (c) 4,

   (d) an even number,

   (e) a number less than 4?

   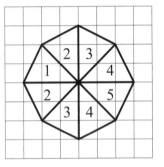

6. A bag of sweets contains 8 mints, 6 toffees and 2 boiled sweets. A sweet is taken at random from the bag. What is the probability that it is:

   (a) a mint,

   (b) a toffee,

   (c) a boiled sweet,

   (d) not a mint,

   (e) not a toffee?

7. In a class there are 18 boys and 12 girls. One child is chosen at random to represent the class. What is the probability that this child is:

   (a) a girl,

   (b) a boy?

8. The diagram shows a piece of card
    that is folded to form a dice.

    When the dice is rolled, what is the
    probability that it shows:

    (a)   a blue face,

    (b)   a red face,

    (c)   a yellow face,

    (d)   a face that is not red,

    (e)   a face that is not yellow?

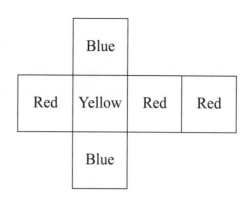

9. The children in a class were asked to name their favourite colour. The
    results are given in the table:

Colour	Number of Children
Red	6
Black	2
Yellow	3
Green	4
Blue	10
Pink	7

    If a child is picked at random from the class, what is the probability that
    their favourite colour is:

    (a)   red,   (b)   yellow,

    (c)   pink   (d)   black,

    (e)   not pink,   (f)   not green?

10. A bag contains 6 red balls and some white balls. When a ball is taken from

    the bag at random, the probability that it is red is $\dfrac{3}{5}$. How many white balls

    are in the bag?

21.3 Relative Frequency

Some probabilities cannot be calculated as in the last section; for example, the probability that it will rain on 20 November cannot be found in this way. Probabilities can, however, be estimated using *relative frequencies* found from observations or from experiments.

$$\text{Relative frequency} = \frac{\text{number of successful trials}}{\text{total number of trials}}$$

Example 1

Matthew decides to try to estimate the probability that toast lands butter-side-down when dropped. He drops a piece of buttered toast 50 times and observes that it lands butter-side-down 30 times.

Estimate the probability that the toast lands butter-side-down.

Solution

An estimate of the probability is given by the relative frequency. In this case this is

$$\frac{30}{50} = \frac{3}{5}$$

Example 2

Sarah tosses a coin 200 times. She gets 108 heads and 92 tails. Using her results, estimate the probability of obtaining:

(a)   a head when the coin is tossed,

(b)   a tail when the coin is tossed.

Solution

The relative frequency gives an estimate of the probability.

(a)   Relative frequency $= \dfrac{108}{200} = \dfrac{27}{50}$

(b)   Relative Frequency $= \dfrac{92}{200} = \dfrac{23}{50}$

We would expect both these probabilities to be $\dfrac{1}{2}$, and here the estimates are close to that value, indicating that her coin may be a fair one.

Example 3

Rachel was testing a coin to see if it was fair. She tossed the coin 50 times and recorded 36 HEADS. She tossed it another 50 times and recorded 32 HEADS. She continued in this way, and recorded her results on the following table:

No. of Tosses	No. of Heads
50	36
50	32
50	30
50	38
50	30
50	36
50	34
50	30

(a) Calculate the total frequency (total number of HEADS) after 50, 100, 150, . . . , 400 throws and also calculate, at each stage, the relative frequency.

(b) Plot the points on a relative frequency graph, and hence estimate the probability of obtaining a head. What should be Rachel's conclusion?

Solution

(a)

No. of Tosses	50	100	150	200	250	300	350	400
Total Frequency	36	68	98	136	166	202	236	266
Relative Frequency	$\frac{36}{50} = 0.72$	$\frac{68}{100} = 0.68$	0.653	0.68	0.664	0.673	0.674	0.665

(b) The relative frequency graph follows, from which we can see that the probability looks to be about 0.665 (or about $\frac{2}{3}$). Rachel should conclude that her coin is probably *not* fair, i.e. the coin probably *is* biased (since, for a fair coin, we would expect the probability to be 0.5; so although the evidence is fairly strong, Rachel cannot be certain that her coin is biased).

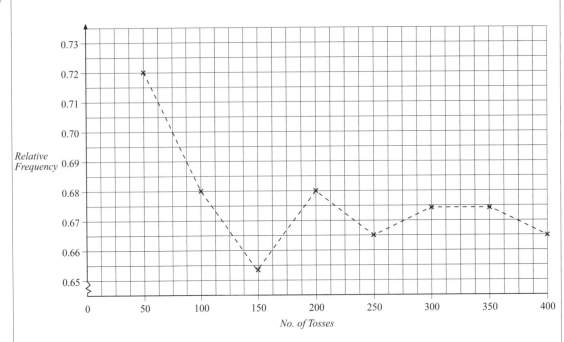

 ## Exercises

1. (a) Toss a coin 100 times. Record your results after every 10 tosses. Plot a relative frequency graph and estimate the probability of obtaining a head when you toss the coin.

    (b) Is your answer to (a) close to $\frac{1}{2}$?

    (c) Put all the results for your class together and obtain a new estimate of the probability of obtaining a head.

    (d) Is your new estimate closer to $\frac{1}{2}$ than the estimate in (a)?

2. A drawing pin can land 'point up' or 'point down' when dropped. Carry out an experiment to find an estimate of the probability that a drawing pin lands 'point up', using a relative frequency graph.

3. (a) Roll a dice 100 times and record the results you obtain.

    (b) Estimate the probability of obtaining each of the numbers on the faces of the dice.

    (c) Do you think that the probabilities that you obtain are reasonable?

    (d) Obtain more results by rolling the dice another 100 times. How do your probability estimates change as you use more results?

4. By considering the people in your class, estimate the probability that a person chosen at random is left-handed.

5. If it rained on 12 days in November last year, estimate the probability that it will rain on 20 November next year.

6. You can make a biased dice out of a hollow cube by sticking a small lump of blu-tac inside the cube.

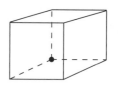

Make a biased dice and use it to estimate the probability of obtaining a 6 on your dice.

7. A calculator can be used to generate random digits. Halim generates 100 random digits with his calculator. He lists the results in the following table:

0	⑷⑷ ‖	5	⑷⑷ ⑷⑷
1	⑷⑷ ‖‖	6	⑷⑷ ‖‖‖
2	⑷⑷ ‖	7	⑷⑷ ⑷⑷ ‖
3	⑷⑷ ⑷⑷ ‖	8	⑷⑷ ⑷⑷
4	⑷⑷ ⑷⑷ ‖	9	⑷⑷ ⑷⑷ ‖‖‖

Based on Halim's results, estimate the probability that the calculator produces:

(a)   9,

(b)   2,

(c)   a digit that is an odd number,

(d)   a digit that is a prime number.

8. Tony estimates that the probability that there will be an empty space in the car park when he arrives at work is $\frac{4}{5}$. His estimate is based on 50 observations. On how many of these 50 days was he *unable* to find an empty space in the car park?

9. Paul draws the bar chart opposite to show the results for his football team so far this season.

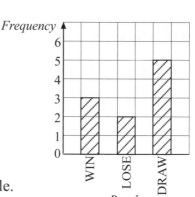

(a)   Use the bar chart to estimate the probability that his team will win their next match.

(b)   Give reasons why this estimate of the probability that they will win their next match may not be very reliable.

10.   Sasha carries out the drawing pin experiment described in question 2. She
      shows her results in this pie chart:

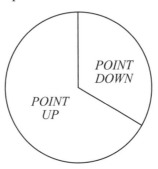

      Use her results to estimate the probability that the pin lands 'point up'.

21.4 Complementary Events

Two events are described as *complementary* if they are the *only two* possible
outcomes. For example, the events A and B below are complementary:

A :   It rains.

B :   It does not rain.

If A is an event and A' is the complementary event,

$$p(A) + p(A') = 1$$

or

$$p(A') = 1 - p(A)$$

Example 1

If the probability that it will rain tomorrow is $\frac{1}{5}$, what is the probability that it will
not rain tomorrow?

Solution

As these are two complementary events,

$$\text{probability that it will not rain tomorrow } = 1 - \frac{1}{5}$$

$$= \frac{4}{5}$$

Example 2

A dice has been renumbered so that the probability of obtaining an even number is now $\frac{2}{3}$. What is the probability of obtaining an odd number?

Solution

As these are two complementary events,

$$\text{probability of obtaining an odd number} = 1 - \frac{2}{3}$$

$$= \frac{1}{3}$$

Complementary events can be illustrated in a Venn diagram:

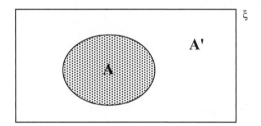

Exercises

1. The probability that Scot will win his next tennis match is $\frac{3}{5}$. What is the probability that he will *not* win?

2. The probability that it will snow on Christmas Day is $\frac{1}{8}$. What is the probability that it will *not* snow on Christmas Day?

3. The probability that a child is left-handed is $\frac{1}{20}$. What is the probability that a child is right-handed?

4. The probability that Natasha is late for school is 0.1. What is the probability that she is *not* late?

5. The probability that Sergio gets all his spellings correct in his next test is 0.75. What is the probability that he does *not* get them all correct?

6. If you take a card at random from a pack of playing cards, the probability that you get a king is $\frac{1}{13}$. What is the probability that you do *not* get a king?

7. One of the numbers in the Venn diagram below is chosen at random.

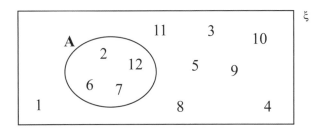

   (a) What is the probability that the number is in the set A?

   (b) What is the probability that the number is *not* in the set A?

8. (a) What is the probability that you will get a prime number when you roll a fair dice?

   (b) What is the probability that you will *not* get a prime number when you roll a fair dice?

9. In one year it rains on 12 days in the month of September.

   (a) Use this information to estimate the probability that it will rain on 19 September next year.

   (b) Use your answer to (a) to make an estimate of the probability that it will not rain on 19 September next year.

10. A bag contains 100 balls, each marked with a number from 1 to 100. A ball is taken from the bag at random.

   (a) What is the probability that the number on the ball is a multiple of 3?

   (b) What is the probability that the number on the ball is *not* a multiple of 3?

21.5 Estimating the Number of Outcomes

If we know the probability of an event we can estimate the number of times we expect that event to take place.

> *Expected number of successful outcomes*
> *= probability of success × total number of outcomes*

Example 1

You toss an unbiased coin 500 times. How many heads should you expect to obtain?

Solution

Probability of a head $= \dfrac{1}{2}$

Expected number of heads $= \dfrac{1}{2} \times 500$

$= 250$

Example 2

You roll a fair dice 120 times. How many times would you expect to obtain:

(a)   a 6,

(b)   a multiple of 3?

Solution

(a)   Probability of a 6 $= \dfrac{1}{6}$

   Expected number of sixes $= \dfrac{1}{6} \times 120$

   $= 20$

(b)   Probability of a multiple of 3 $= \dfrac{1}{3}$

   Expected number of multiples of 3 $= \dfrac{1}{3} \times 120$

   $= 40$

Exercises

1.   If you roll an unbiased dice 600 times, how many times would you expect to obtain:

   (a)   a one,

   (b)   an *even* number,

   (c)   an *odd* number,

   (d)   a number less than 3?

2.   A spinner is marked with the numbers 1 to 5, each of which is equally likely to occur when the spinner is spun. If it is spun 200 times, how many times would you expect to obtain:

   (a)   a five,

   (b)   an even number,

   (c)   a number less than 3,

   (d)   a prime number?

3.   If the probability that it rains on a day in September is $\frac{1}{5}$, on how many days in September would you expect it to rain?

4.   When you open a packet of sweets and take one out at random, the probability that it is blue is $\frac{1}{8}$. If you open 40 packets of sweets, how many times would you expect to take out a blue sweet *first*?

5.   Some crisp packets contain prizes. The probability that you find a prize in a crisp packet is $\frac{1}{25}$. How many prizes would you expect to find if you opened:

   (a)   50 packets,

   (b)   200 packets,

   (c)   1000 packets?

6.   The probability that Joshua misses the school bus is $\frac{3}{10}$. In a school year there are 40 weeks, each of 5 days.

   How many times can you expect Joshua to miss the bus in:

   (a)   a 12-week term,

   (b)   a school year?

7. The probability that a person, selected at random, has been trained in First Aid is $\frac{1}{50}$. How many people trained in First Aid would you expect to find in:

    (a) a crowd of 50 000 spectators at a football match,

    (b) an audience of 300 at a theatre,

    (c) a group of 50 onlookers at the scene of an accident?

8. The probability that a certain type of seed germinates is 0.7. How many seeds would you expect to germinate if you planted:

    (a) 20 seeds,

    (b) 70 seeds,

    (c) 1000 seeds?

9. The probability that Emma wins a game of 'Freecell' on her computer is $\frac{2}{5}$. She wants to be able to say that she has won 5 games. How many games should she expect to play before she wins 5 games?

10. Prakesh says that the probability that he misses the school bus is $\frac{1}{10}$.

    (a) How many times would you expect him to miss the bus in 4 weeks?

    (b) In 4 weeks he actually misses the bus 3 times, which is not the same as your answer to (a). Explain why your answer to (a) is still correct.

21.6 Addition Law for Mutually Exclusive Events

Two events are *mutually exclusive* if only *one* can take place at any given time. For example, if a bag contains red balls and yellow balls, when a ball is taken out it is either red or yellow, but it cannot be both. The events 'red ball' and 'yellow ball' are therefore *mutually exclusive*.

> If two events, A and B, are mutually exclusive,
>
> $$p(A \text{ or } B) = p(A) + p(B)$$
>
> where $p(A)$ = probability of A
>
> and $p(B)$ = probability of B

Example 1

A bag contains 6 red balls, 8 yellow balls and 4 green balls. One ball is taken at random from the bag.

What is the probability that the ball is:

(a)　yellow,

(b)　green,

(c)　yellow or green?

Solution

(a)　$p(\text{yellow}) = \dfrac{8}{18}$

$\qquad\qquad\qquad = \dfrac{4}{9}$

(b)　$p(\text{green}) = \dfrac{4}{18}$

$\qquad\qquad\qquad = \dfrac{2}{9}$

(c)　$p(\text{yellow or green}) = p(\text{yellow}) + p(\text{green})$

$\qquad\qquad\qquad\qquad\qquad = \dfrac{4}{9} + \dfrac{2}{9}$

$\qquad\qquad\qquad\qquad\qquad = \dfrac{6}{9}$

$\qquad\qquad\qquad\qquad\qquad = \dfrac{2}{3}$

Example 2

Ten children were asked to state their favourite sport. Their responses are listed in this table:

Favourite Sport	Number of Children
Swimming	4
Hockey	1
Tennis	1
Volleyball	1
Football	3

What is the probability that, if one of the children is chosen at random, their favourite sport will be:

(a)　volleyball,　　　　(b)　swimming,　　　　(c)　volleyball or swimming?

Solution

(a) $p(\text{volleyball}) = \dfrac{1}{10}$

(b) $p(\text{swimming}) = \dfrac{4}{10}$

$$= \dfrac{2}{5}$$

(c) $p(\text{volleyball or swimming}) = p(\text{volleyball}) + p(\text{swimming})$

$$= \dfrac{1}{10} + \dfrac{4}{10}$$

$$= \dfrac{5}{10}$$

$$= \dfrac{1}{2}$$

Exercises

1.   A bag contains 6 red balls, 5 blue balls and 9 yellow balls. A ball is taken at random from the bag. What is the probability that it is:

   (a)   red,

   (b)   blue,

   (c)   yellow,

   (d)   red or blue,

   (e)   red or yellow,

   (f)   blue or yellow?

2.   In a packet of sweets there are 20 mints, 10 fudges and 20 toffees. A sweet is taken at random from the packet. What is the probability that it is:

   (a)   a fudge,

   (b)   a toffee,

   (c)   a mint,

   (d)   a mint or a toffee,

   (e)   a mint or a fudge,

   (f)   a toffee or a fudge?

3.   A group of children were asked their ages. These are recorded in the table opposite:

Age (in years)	Number of Children
10	4
11	14
12	16
13	6

What is the probability that a child selected at random from the group, is:

(a) age 10,

(b) age 10 or 11,

(c) age 12 or 13,

(d) age 11 or 12?

4. In the school canteen, children can choose one of baked potato, chips or rice for lunch. The probability that a child chooses a baked potato is $\frac{1}{6}$, the probability that they choose chips is $\frac{2}{3}$ and the probability that they choose rice is $\frac{1}{6}$.

What is the probability that a child chooses:

(a) rice or baked potato,

(b) rice or chips,

(c) chips or baked potato?

5. Zahra buys a mobile phone with 5 different coloured covers. The probability of her using each cover is given in the table opposite.

What is the probability that she uses:

(a) a red or a pink cover,

(b) a green or a red cover,

(c) a yellow or a blue cover,

(d) a pink or a yellow cover?

Colour	Probability
Red	$\frac{1}{8}$
Blue	$\frac{1}{4}$
Green	$\frac{1}{16}$
Yellow	$\frac{1}{16}$
Pink	$\frac{1}{2}$

6. In his pocket, Andy has the coins below:

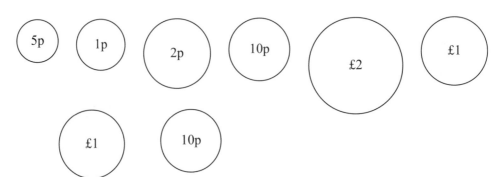

He takes a coin at random from his pocket.

What is the probability that it is:

(a)   a £1 or a £2 coin,

(b)   a 1p or a 2p coin,

(c)   a 5p or a 10p coin,

(d)   a 1p or a £1 coin?

7.   Alex can walk to school, cycle to school or go by bus. The probability that he walks or cycles to school is $\frac{3}{4}$.

(a)   If the probability that he cycles is $\frac{1}{4}$, what is the probability that he walks?

(b)   What is the probability that he goes by bus?

(c)   What is the probability that he cycles or goes by bus?

8.   A bus can arrive early, on time or late. The probability that it is late is $\frac{1}{4}$.

The probability that it is on time or late is $\frac{2}{3}$.

(a)   What is the probability that the bus is on time?

(b)   What is the probability that it is early or on time?

9.   A bag contains 30 coloured balls. Of these, 10 are red, 6 are blue and the rest are green or yellow.

A ball is taken at random from the bag. The probability that this ball is yellow is $\frac{1}{6}$.

What is the probability that a ball taken at random from the bag is:

(a)   green,

(b)   green or yellow,

(c)   red or blue,

(d)   red, blue or yellow?

10.   A bag contains red, yellow and green balls. One ball is taken at random from the bag. The probability that it is red or green is $\frac{1}{2}$. The probability that it is yellow or green is $\frac{3}{4}$.

What is the probability that a ball taken at random from the bag is:

(a)   green,

(b)   red or yellow?

21.7   General Addition Law

Events may not always be mutually exclusive. For example, if you roll a dice, the events 'getting a six' and 'getting an even number' are *not* mutually exclusive. In this section we consider examples of this type.

$$p(\text{A or B}) = p(\text{A}) + p(\text{B}) - p(\text{A and B})$$

This can be shown using a *Venn diagram*.

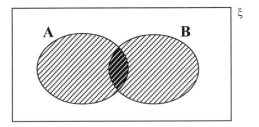

The *union* (A or B) is shaded, whilst the *intersection* (A and B) is double shaded.

So, if there are n possible events, with

         number of events in only A $= x$

         number of events in only B $= y$

         number of events in both A and B $= z$

         number of events in neither A nor B $= w,$

this can be illustrated in the following Venn diagram:

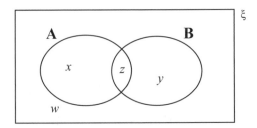

Thus

$$p(A) \qquad = \frac{x+z}{n}$$

$$p(B) \qquad = \frac{y+z}{n}$$

$$p(A \text{ and } B) \ = \frac{z}{n}$$

and $\qquad p(A \text{ or } B) \quad = \frac{x+z+y}{n}$

Now $\qquad p(A) + p(B) - p(A \text{ and } B) \ = \left(\frac{x+z}{n}\right) + \left(\frac{y+z}{n}\right) - \left(\frac{z}{n}\right)$

$$= \frac{x+z+y+z-z}{n}$$

$$= \frac{x+z+y}{n}$$

$$= \ p(A \text{ or } B)$$

and so the result is true.

Example 1

One of the numbers 1 to 10 is selected at random. What is the probability that it is:

(a)   an even number,

(b)   greater than 5,

(c)   an even number *and* greater than 5,

(d)   an even number *or* greater than 5.

Solution

A Venn diagram is helpful for problems like this.

Let:

         A be the set of even numbers

and   B be the set of numbers greater than 5.

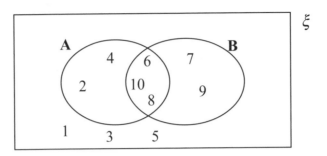

(a) $p(\text{an even number}) = p(A)$

$$= \frac{5}{10}$$

$$= \frac{1}{2}$$

(b) $p(\text{greater than 5}) = \frac{5}{10}$

$$= \frac{1}{2}$$

(c) $p(\text{even \textit{and} greater than 5}) = p(A \text{ and } B)$

$$= \frac{3}{10}$$

(d) $p(\text{even \textit{or} greater than 5}) = p(A) + p(B) - p(A \text{ and } B)$

$$= \frac{1}{2} + \frac{1}{2} - \frac{3}{10}$$

$$= \frac{7}{10}$$

 ## Example 2

A dice is rolled. What is the probability of getting a prime number or an even number?

 ## Solution

$p(\text{even number}) = \dfrac{3}{6}$ (since there are 3 even numbers, 2, 4 and 6)

$$= \frac{1}{2}$$

$$p(\text{prime number}) = \frac{3}{6} \qquad \text{(since there are 3 prime numbers, 2, 3 and 5)}$$

$$= \frac{1}{2}$$

$$p(\text{even } \textit{and} \text{ prime number}) = \frac{1}{6} \quad \text{(since there is one even, prime number, namely 2)}$$

$$p(\text{even } \textit{or} \text{ prime}) = p(\text{even}) + p(\text{prime}) - p(\text{even and prime})$$

$$= \frac{1}{2} + \frac{1}{2} - \frac{1}{6}$$

$$= \frac{5}{6}$$

Exercises

1. One of the numbers 10 to 20 is selected at random. What is the probability that it is:

    (a) an even number,

    (b) a multiple of 5,

    (c) an even number *and* a multiple of 5,

    (d) an even number *or* a multiple of 5?

2. The numbers 1 to 10 are sorted into sets as shown in the Venn diagram:

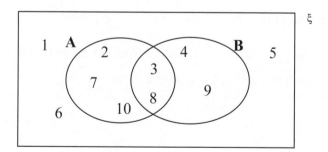

    One of these numbers is selected at random. What is the probability that it is a member of:

    (a) A,

    (b) B,

    (c) A *and* B,

    (d) A *or* B?

3. A fair dice is rolled. What is the probability of getting a prime number *or* an odd number?

4. One of the numbers 1 to 20 is selected at random. What is the probability that the number is a multiple of 3 *or* a multiple of 4?

5. A bingo set contains 100 balls each marked with one of the numbers 1 to 100. One of these balls is selected at random. What it the probability that the number on this ball is a multiple of 7 or of 10?

6. If $p(A) = \dfrac{3}{4}$, $p(B) = \dfrac{3}{8}$ and $p(A \text{ and } B) = \dfrac{1}{3}$, find $p(A \text{ or } B)$.

7. If $p(A \text{ or } B) = \dfrac{3}{5}$, $p(A \text{ and } B) = \dfrac{2}{5}$ and $p(A) = \dfrac{1}{2}$, find $p(B)$.

8. If $p(A \text{ or } B) = \dfrac{1}{2}$, $p(A) = \dfrac{2}{5}$ and $p(B) = \dfrac{1}{3}$, find $p(A \text{ and } B)$.

9. The probability that Jai is late for school is 0.1. The probability that he forgets his lunch is 0.3. The probability that he forgets his lunch *and* is late is 0.05.

   What is the probability that he forgets his lunch or is late?

10. The faces of a dice are marked with the numbers 1, 2, 3 or 4. This is done so that the probability of rolling a 3 is $\dfrac{1}{6}$, the probability of rolling a 3 or a 4 is $\dfrac{1}{3}$ and the probability of rolling a prime or an even number is $\dfrac{2}{3}$. How often does each number appear on the dice?

22 Volume

22.1 Concept of Volume: the Unit Cube

In this section we look at volume for the first time, by counting the number of 1 cm cubes in a solid.

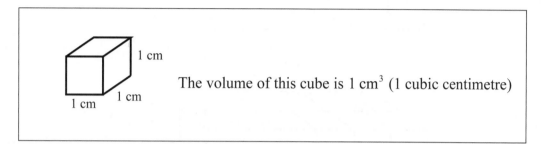

The volume of this cube is 1 cm³ (1 cubic centimetre)

Example 1

What is the volume of this solid:

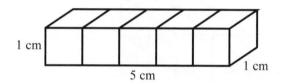

Solution

The solid contains 5 cubes of side 1 cm, so the volume is 5 cm³.

Example 2

What is the volume of this solid:

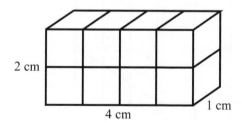

Solution

This solid contains 8 cubes of side 1 cm, so the volume is 8 cm³.

22.1

Exercises

1. What is the volume of each of these cuboids:

    (a)

    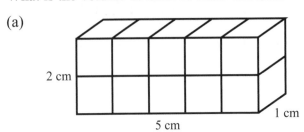

    (b)

    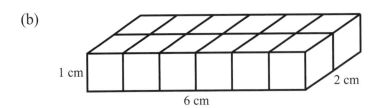

    (c)

    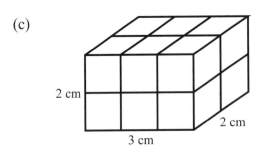

    (d)

    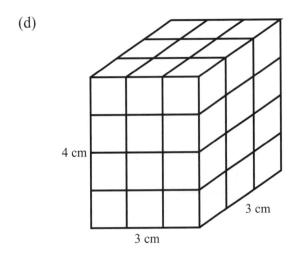

2. What is the volume of each of these solids:

(a)

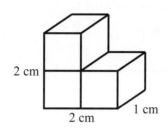

(b)

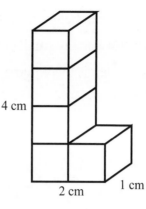

(c)

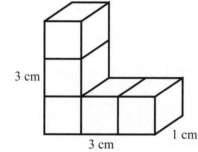

3. The diagram shows the cubes that are used to make the first layer of a cuboid:

(a) How many cubes are there in the first layer?

(b) What is the volume of the cuboid if it is made up of 6 layers?

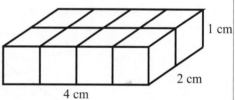

4. A cuboid is built from 1 cm cubes on top of this rectangular base:

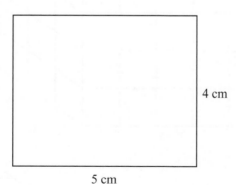

(a) How many cubes are there in the first layer?

(b) If there are 4 layers, what is the volume of the cuboid?

5.   The diagram below shows a large cube made from 1 cm cubes.

   (a)   How many small cubes are in each layer of the large cube?

   (b)   What is the volume of the large cube?

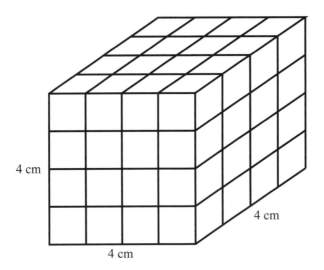

6.   What is the volume of this cube:

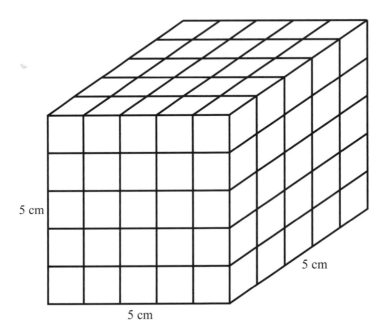

7.   (a)   What is the volume of the cube
           shown in the diagram opposite?

     (b)   The top layer is cut off.
           What is the volume of the
           solid that remains?

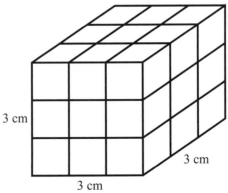

8. Sally is asked to make a cuboid with sides of length 7 cm, 3 cm and 4 cm. She runs out of cubes when she has made the shape in the diagram:

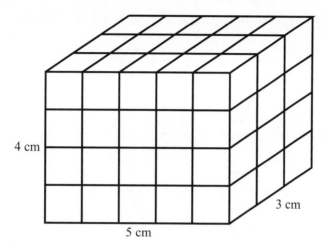

(a) What is the volume of the shape she has made?

(b) How many more cubes would she need to make the required shape?

9. How many of each of these shapes would be needed to make a 1 cm cube?

What is the volume of each of these shapes:

(a)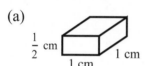

(b)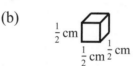

10. What is the volume of each of these shapes:

(a)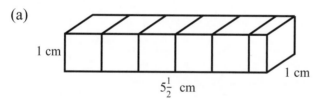

(b)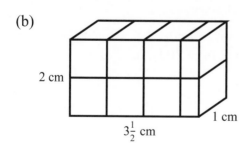

22.2 Volume of a Cube

In this section we consider the volume of a cube and the units of volume.

Volume of a cube $= a \times a \times a$

$= a^3$

where a is the length of the each side of the cube

Note: If the sides of the cube are measured in cm, the volume will be measured in cm^3.

Example 1

What is the volume of this cube:

Solution

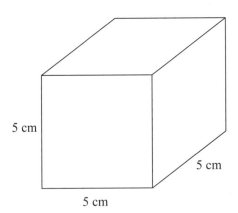

Volume $= 5^3$

$= 5 \times 5 \times 5$

$= 125 \ cm^3$

Example 2

What is the volume of this cube in:

(a) m^3,

(b) cm^3?

Solution

(a)   Volume $= 2^3$

$= 2 \times 2 \times 2$

$= 8 \ m^3$

(b)   Remember that 1 m = 100 cm, so 2 m = 200 cm.

Volume $= 200^3$

$= 200 \times 200 \times 200$

$= 8\,000\,000 \ cm^3$

$$1 \ m^3 \ = \ 1\,000\,000 \ cm^3$$

Exercises

1. What is the volume of each of these cubes:

   (a)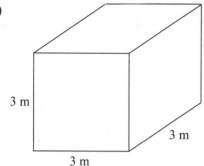

   3 m

   3 m

   3 m

   (b)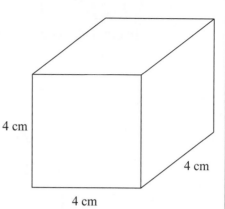

   4 cm

   4 cm

   4 cm

   (c)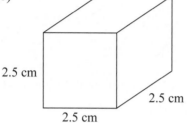

   2.5 cm

   2.5 cm

   2.5 cm

   (d)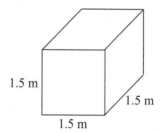

   1.5 m

   1.5 m

   1.5 m

2. A cube has sides of length 30 cm. What is the volume of the cube in:

   (a) cm^3,

   (b) m^3?

3. A large box is a cube with sides of length 80 cm. Smaller boxes, which are also cubes, have sides of lengths 20 cm.

   (a) What is the volume of the large box?

   (b) What is the volume of a small box?

   (c) How many small boxes will fit in the large box?

4. A cube has sides of length $\frac{1}{2}$ m.

   Calculate the volume of the cube:

   (a) in m^3, giving your answer as a fraction,

   (b) in m^3, giving your answer as a decimal,

   (c) in cm^3.

5.   A cube has sides of length 10 cm. Calculate the volume of the cube in:

      (a)   cm^3,   (b)   m^3.

6.   The diagram shows a cube with sides of length 30 cm. A smaller cube with
      sides of length 5 cm has been cut out of the larger cube.

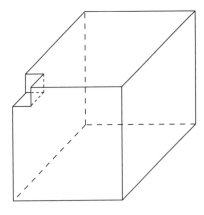

      (a)   What is the volume of the large cube before the small cube is cut out?

      (b)   What is the volume of the small cube?

      (c)   What is the volume of the shape that is left?

7.   Wooden building blocks are cubes with sides of length 4 cm. A child builds
      a tower 6 blocks high. What is the volume of the tower?

8.   This 'staircase' is built from wooden
      cubes with sides of length 6 cm.

      (a)   What is the volume of the staircase?

      (b)   A similar staircase is 4 blocks high
             instead of 3. What is the volume
             of this staircase?

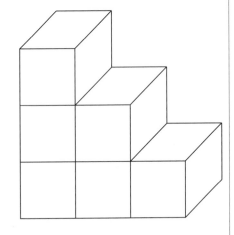

9.   A cube has volume 343 cm^3.

      (a)   How long are the sides of the cube?

      (b)   What is the area of one face of the cube?

      (c)   What is the total area of the surface of the cube?

10.   The area of one face of a cube is 81 cm^2.
      What is the volume of the cube?

22.3 Volume of a Cuboid

We now consider the volume of any cuboid.

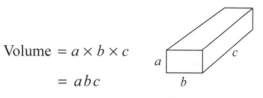

Volume $= a \times b \times c$

$= abc$

where a, b and c are the lengths
of the sides of the cuboid

Example 1

Calculate the volume of this cuboid:

Solution

Volume $= 3 \times 4 \times 7$

$= 84 \text{ cm}^3$

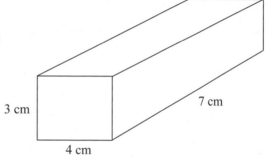

Example 2

A letter 'T' shape is made by sticking together 2 cuboids as shown in the diagram.
What is the total volume of the letter 'T' ?

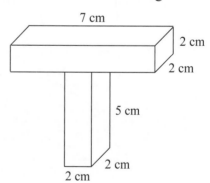

Solution

First find the volume of the top cuboid:

Volume $= 7 \times 2 \times 2$

$= 28 \text{ cm}^3$

Then find the volume of the upright cuboid:

Volume $= 2 \times 2 \times 5$

$= 20 \text{ cm}^3$

These two volumes can then be added to give the total volume:

Total volume $= 28 + 20$

$= 48 \text{ cm}^3$

Exercises

1. Calculate the volume of each of these cuboids:

(a)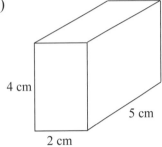

(b)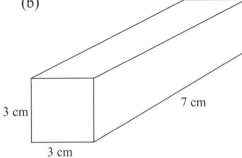

(c)

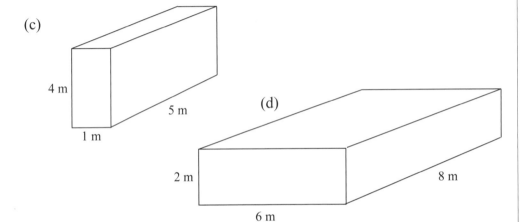

(d)

2. A cuboid has sides of length 5 m, 3 m and 1 m. What is the volume of the cuboid in:

   (a) m^3,   (b) cm^3?

3. The diagram shows a large box and a small box, both of which are cuboids.

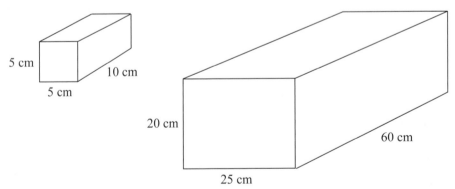

   (a) Calculate the volume of the large box.

   (b) Calculate the volume of the small box.

   (c) How many of the small boxes would fit in the large box?

4. A set of wooden building blocks contains wooden blocks that are 10 cm by 2 cm by 4 cm. The blocks are used to make the shapes below.

Calculate the volume of each shape.

(a)

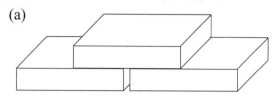

(b)

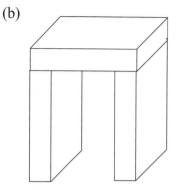

5. Calculate the volume of this cuboid, giving your answer:

(a)   in m^3, using fractions,

(b)   in m^3, using decimals,

(c)   in cm^3.

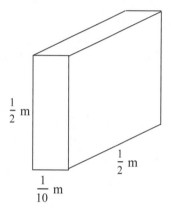

6. A letter 'L' shape is made from two cuboids.

(a)   Calculate the volume of each cuboid.

(b)   Calculate the volume of this letter 'L' shape.

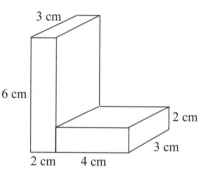

7. Calculate the volume of this solid:

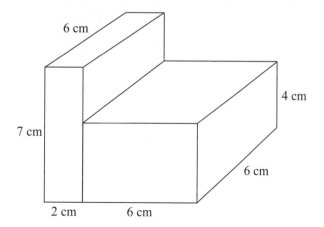

8. The diagram shows a wooden block that has had a square hole cut through it. Calculate the volume of wood in the block.

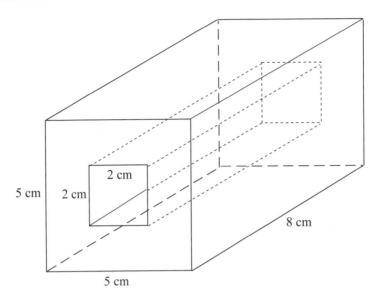

9. The diagram shows a cuboid. The area of the shaded end is 8 cm^2.

    How long is the cuboid if its volume is:

    (a) 80 cm^3,

    (b) 96 cm^3,

    (c) 20 cm^3?

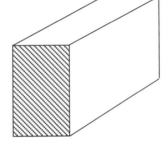

10. The shape in the diagram can be folded to form a cuboid. Calculate the volume of the cuboid.

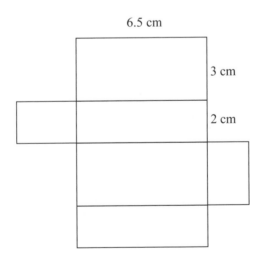

22.4 Capacity

When we refer to how much liquid a tank or container can hold, we often talk about its *capacity* in litres. This is another way of describing its volume.

$$1000 \text{ cm}^3 = 1 \text{ litre}$$

Example 1

What is the capacity, in litres, of a tank with dimensions 1 m by 1 m by 1 m?

Solution

Working in centimetres,

$$\text{Volume} = 100 \times 100 \times 100$$

$$= 1\,000\,000 \text{ cm}^3$$

$$\text{Capacity (in litres)} = \frac{1\,000\,000}{1000}$$

$$= 1000 \text{ litres}$$

Note that the volume of this tank is also 1 m^3, so $1 \text{ m}^3 = 1000$ litres.

$$1 \text{ m}^3 = 1000 \text{ litres}$$

Example 2

A tank measures 3 m by 4 m by 2 m. What is the capacity of the tank in litres?

Solution

$$\text{Volume} = 3 \times 4 \times 2$$

$$= 24 \text{ m}^3$$

$$\text{But} \qquad 1 \text{ m}^3 = 1000 \text{ litres}$$

$$\text{so} \qquad \text{capacity} = 24 \times 1000$$

$$= 24\,000 \text{ litres}$$

Example 3

Calculate the volume of a bottle of capacity 700 cm^3.

Solution

Volume $= \dfrac{700}{1000}$

$\qquad = 0.7$ litres

Exercises

1. Convert these volumes into cm^3:

    (a) 2 litres   (b) 5 litres   (c) $\dfrac{1}{2}$ litre

    (d) 0.2 litres   (e) 1.5 litres   (f) 2.7 litres

2. Convert these volumes into litres:

    (a) 3000 cm^3 (b) 7000 cm^3 (c) 10 000 cm^3

    (d) 750 cm^3 (e) 250 cm^3 (f) 4900 cm^3

3. A tank has dimensions 3 m by 3 m by 2 m.
    Calculate the capacity of the tank in:
    (a) m^3 (b) litres.

4. A tank holds 5000 litres. Calculate the volume of the tank in m^3.

5. Work out which of these tanks has the greatest capacity:

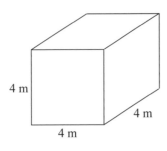
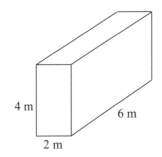
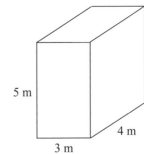

     A   B   C

6. A large bottle holds 2 litres of lemonade. The lemonade is poured out into glasses that each hold 25 cm³. How many glasses can be filled?

7. The diagram shows 2 different tanks:

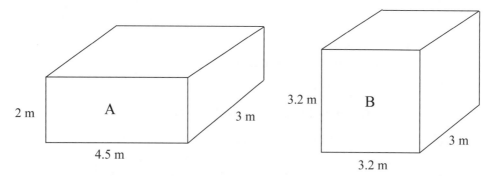

    (a)   Which tank has the greater capacity?

    (b)   How many more litres does the larger tank hold than the smaller one?

8. The base of a tank is 1.5 m by 2.5 m and its height is 2 m. It is part full of water.

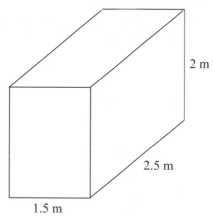

    (a)   What is the volume of water in the tank, in litres, if the water is 1.2 m deep?

    (b)   How many litres of water does the tank contain when it is $\frac{1}{4}$ full?

    (c)   How deep is the water when the tank contains 3000 litres?

9. A tank contains 12.5 litres of liquid. Cans of capacity 800 cm³ are filled from the tank.

    (a)   How many cans can be filled from the tank?

    (b)   How much liquid is left over?

10. Ben puts a rock in the tank shown in the diagram and then fills the tank to the top with water. Then he takes the rock out and the water level drops by 5 cm.

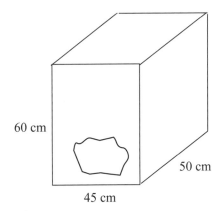

60 cm

50 cm

45 cm

(a) What is the capacity of the tank when it is full?

(b) What is the volume of water in the tank when the rock has been taken out?

(c) Calculate the volume of the rock, in cm³.

(d) How many litres of water would be needed to fill the tank to the top again?

22.5 Density

If you were to fill boxes of the same capacity with different materials you would find some easier to lift than others. For example, a box of sand would be much heavier than a box of polystyrene beads. We say that sand is more *dense* than polystyrene. Density, mass and volume are connected by the relationships:

$$\text{Density} = \frac{\text{mass}}{\text{volume}}$$

$$\text{Mass} = \text{density} \times \text{volume}$$

$$\text{Volume} = \frac{\text{mass}}{\text{density}}$$

Mercury (the only metal which is liquid at room temperature) has a density of $13\ 600\ \text{kg/m}^3$; air has density $1.4\ \text{kg/m}^3$ and water $1000\ \text{kg/m}^3$ or $1\ \text{gram/cm}^3$.

Example 1

Calculate the mass of 3 litres of water.

Solution

$3 \text{ litres } = 3000 \text{ cm}^3$

$\text{Mass} = \text{density} \times \text{volume}$

$\phantom{\text{Mass}} = 1 \times 3000$

= 3000 grams

= 3 kg

Example 2

This metal block has mass 2 kg.

Calculate the density of the metal in:

(a)   grams/cm^3,

(b)   kg/cm^3.

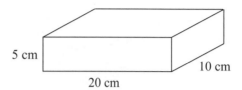

5 cm

10 cm

20 cm

Solution

First find the volume of the block:

Volume $= 5 \times 20 \times 10$

$= 1000 \ cm^3$

(a)   Note that 2 kg = 2000 grams.

Density $= \dfrac{mass}{volume}$

$= \dfrac{2000}{1000}$

$= 2$ grams/cm^3

(b)   Density $= \dfrac{mass}{volume}$

$= \dfrac{2}{1000}$

$= 0.002$ kg/cm^3

Example 3

A type of wood has density 0.7 grams/cm^3. A piece of this wood is 3 cm by 10 cm by 180 cm.

What is the mass of this piece of wood, in:

(a)   grams   (b)   kg?

Solution

(a)   First calculate the volume of the wood:

   Volume $= 3 \times 10 \times 180$

                $= 5400 \text{ cm}^3$

   Mass $=$ density $\times$ volume

              $= 0.7 \times 5400$

              $= 3780 \text{ grams}$

(b)   3780 grams $= 3.78$ kg

Exercises

1.   Calculate the mass of the following volumes of water:

   (a) 100 cm^3 (b)   2 litres   (c)   0.5 litres.

2.   The mass of the metal block below is 3 kg.

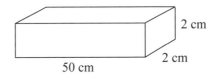

2 cm

2 cm

50 cm

   What is the density of the block, in:

   (a) kg/cm^3,

   (b) grams/cm^3?

3.   A polystyrene block has dimensions 1 m by 2 m by 3 m. The mass of the block is 24 kg.

   (a)   Calculate the density of the polystyrene in grams/cm^3.

   (b)   A smaller block of polystyrene has dimensions 50 cm by 20 cm by 30 cm. What is its mass?

4. The diagram shows a tank that is to be filled with water. Calculate the mass of water, in kg, if the tank is to be:

   (a) full,

   (b) $\frac{1}{2}$ full.

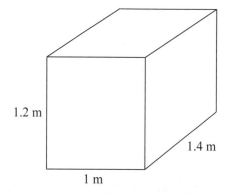

1.2 m

1.4 m

1 m

5. A rectangular block of metal, 5 cm by 8 cm by 10 cm, has a mass of 500 grams. Calculate the density of the metal in

   (a) g/cm^3,

   (b) kg/cm^3.

6. A book has dimensions 1 cm by 24 cm by 30 cm. Its mass is 576 grams.

   (a) Calculate the density of the book.

   (b) What is the mass of a book with dimensions 1.5 cm by 20 cm by 15 cm?

7. The density of concrete is 4 grams/cm^3.

   (a) Calculate the mass of a concrete block with dimensions 10 cm by 45 cm by 22 cm.

   (b) Calculate the volume of a concrete block with a mass of 5 kg.

8. A box with dimensions 6 cm by 5 cm by 2 cm is full of soil. The mass of the soil in the box is 72 grams.

   (a) Calculate the density of the soil.

   (b) Calculate the mass of soil, in kg, needed to fill a window box which has dimensions 70 cm by 20 cm by 25 cm.

9. The density of sea water is *not* the same as the density of pure water.

   When this tank is filled with sea water the mass of the water is 82 400 kg.

   (a) If the tank was filled with pure water, what would be the mass of the water?

   (b) Does pure water or sea water have the higher density?

   (c) What is the density of sea water in grams/cm^3?

   (d) What is the mass of 1 litre of sea water?

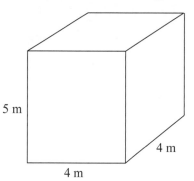

5 m

4 m

4 m

10. One type of metal has a density of 4 grams/cm^3. Another type has a density of 5 grams/cm^3. Weights are made from both types of metal.

Calculate the difference in volume of 500 gram weights made from the two types of metal.

22.6 Volume of a Triangular Prism

We now look at how to find the volume of a triangular prism. You will need to remember how to find the area of a triangle in order to do this:

area of triangle $= \dfrac{1}{2} \times$ base $\times$ perpendicular height

$= \dfrac{1}{2} \times b \times h$

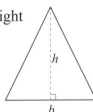

A triangular prism has the same triangular cross-section throughout its length.

Volume of triangular prism $=$ area of cross-section $\times$ length

$= \dfrac{1}{2} \times b \times h \times l$

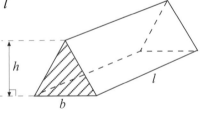

Example 1

The diagram opposite shows a triangular prism.

The area of the end of the prism is 10 cm^3.

Calculate the volume of the prism, if:

(a) $l = 5$ cm, (b) $l = 2$ m.

Solution

(a) Volume $=$ area of cross-section $\times$ length

$= 10 \times 5$

$= 50$ cm^3

(b)   2 m   = 200 cm

   Volume   = area of cross-section × length

              = 10 × 200

              = 2000 cm^3

Example 2

Calculate the volume of this triangular prism:

Solution

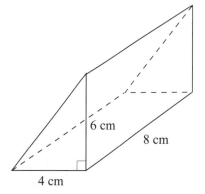

Area of cross-section $= \dfrac{1}{2}$ base × height

                        $= \dfrac{1}{2} \times 4 \times 6$

                        $= 12$ cm^2

Volume of prism = area of cross-section × length

                 $= 12 \times 8$

                 $= 96$ cm^3

Example 3

The triangular prism opposite has a volume of 82 cm^3.
Calculate the area of the shaded part of the prism.

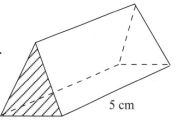

Solution

Volume = area of cross-section × length

   82 = shaded area × 5

Shaded area $= \dfrac{82}{5}$

              $= 16.4$ cm^2

22.6

Exercises

1. Calculate the volume of each of these triangular prisms:

(a)

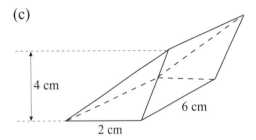

5 cm²

6 cm

(b)

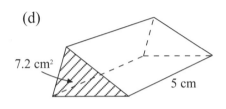

6 cm

8 cm

3 cm

(c)

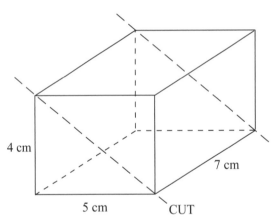

4 cm

6 cm

2 cm

(d)

7.2 cm²

5 cm

2. Two triangular prisms are formed by cutting the rectangular block below, as shown.

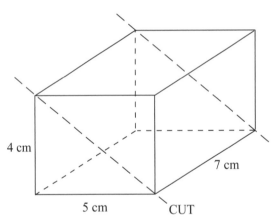

4 cm

7 cm

5 cm   CUT

Calculate the volume of each of the triangular prisms formed.

3. Two identical triangular prisms are stuck together to form a rectangular block. One prism is shown opposite.

(a) What is the volume of this prism?

(b) What is the volume of the rectangular block formed when the two prisms are stuck together?

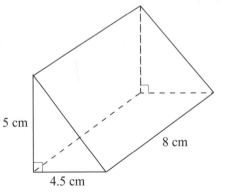

5 cm

8 cm

4.5 cm